FUNDAMENTALS
OF
BOTANY
SERIES

REPRODUCTION,

HEREDITY,

AND SEXUALITY

FUNDAMENTALS OF BOTANY SERIES

edited by
WILLIAM A. JENSEN,
University of California
LEROY G. KAVALJIAN,
Sacramento State College

Stanton A. Cook

UNIVERSITY OF OREGON

REPRODUCTION, HEREDITY, AND SEXUALITY

WADSWORTH PUBLISHING COMPANY, INC.
Belmont, California

L. C. Cat. Card No.: 64–21771

Printed in the United States of America

FOREWORD

Because of the immensity and complexity of the field of botany, the great diversity of plants, and the many methods of plant study, the problem of how to present to the student the highlights of botanical knowledge gained over centuries is not easy to solve. The authors and editors of the volumes in this series believe that an understanding of plants—their parts, their activities, and their relationship to man—is of fundamental importance in appreciating the significance of life. To stress this concept, the form and function of plants, tissues, and cells are treated together. At all levels of organization, in each volume, information gathered by morphologists, physiologists, cytologists, taxonomists, geneticists, biochemists, and ecologists is combined.

Thus, in the volume on *The Plant Cell* by William A. Jensen, the structure and function of the various cell parts are discussed together —for example, mitochondria and respiration, photosynthesis and chloroplasts. The volume by Stanton A. Cook, *Reproduction, Heredity, and Sexuality,* combines the principles of genetics with the means of reproduction in the various plant groups. *Nonvascular Plants: Form and Function,* by William T. Doyle, and *Vascular Plants: Form and Function,* by Frank B. Salisbury and Robert V. Parke, cover the major plant groups and discuss the plants in terms of morphology, physiology, and biochemistry. The relation of plants, particularly vascular plants, to their environment and to each other is covered in *Plants and the Ecosystem* by W. D. Billings. The form and distribution of plants of the past and their relation to the concepts of evolution are considered by Harlan Banks in *Evolution and Plants of the Past.* Herbert G. Baker, in *Plants and Civilization,* discusses the importance of plants to man's social and economic development and the equally important consideration of man's role in the modification and distribution of plants.

In a series such as this, the editors are faced with the task of dividing a broad field into areas that can be presented in a meaningful way by the authors. There must be logic in the entire scheme, with few gaps and a minimum of overlap. Yet an instructor may not want to use the series of volumes in the sequence and manner preferred by the editors. Consequently, each volume must be usable alone and also in any sequence with the others. To achieve such a high degree of versatility is difficult, but we believe the series exhibits these features.

A concerted effort has been made by the authors and editors to maintain a consistent level of presentation. However, each author has been encouraged to approach his subject in his own way and to write in his own style in order to provide variety and to exploit the uniqueness of the individual author's viewpoint. Finally, while presenting the principles of botany we have tried to communicate the excitement of recent developments as well as the joy that comes with the extension of knowledge in any field.

This volume considers the questions of why organisms must reproduce, how their development and mode of reproduction is related to their environment, how like begets both like and unlike, and what sex in botany means. The framework is constructed from knowledge at all levels: molecule, cell, organism, and population. Chapters 2 through 6 deal with genetics—the transmission of characteristics and control of development. Chapters 7 through 10 are concerned with the adaptive and evolutionary significance of various systems of reproduction. Thus, the book goes in two directions: toward the lower levels of molecular genetics, and toward higher levels of adaptation of populations. It examines the forests as well as the trees that make them up, and thus attempts to escape the paradox we are said to be caught in—of learning more and more about less and less as science advances.

CONTENTS

1

FUNDAMENTAL

CONCEPTS

Sex, sex—the term is so rich with implications, and we use it in so many contexts. Most often its mention brings to mind some behavioral or psychological aspect that is really incidental to its central significance—which is that it allows organisms to recombine their attributes at the same time that they reproduce. In other words, the essence of sex is that it allows new combinations of characteristics to arise in organisms. And this potentiality has allowed living things to change with changing environments in space and time. It is this biological change that is called *evolution*.

Seen in this way, sex is but an aspect of a more general phenomenon, *reproduction*. Everything must reproduce, for no living system is eternal. But how shall we study such a broad topic? We must study it at many levels: the cellular level, where transmission of information for growth and differentiation occurs; the level of the whole organism, where form and behavior contribute to initiate and consummate the reproductive event; and the level of the population, where makeup and behavior of the population affect its variation in time.

This book deals with plants, but the principles developed are applicable to all reproducing systems, such as animals and viruses. In fact, frequently the principles have first been found in these other organisms and then been found to be applicable to plants. Dividing the study of natural phenomena into chemistry, physics, and biology—and biology into zoology, botany, and bacteriology—is, after all, a crude and arbitrary simplification. We will focus on plants and the particular problems they present, but we will not shy away from situations found in other forms.

We shall begin with an exploration into inheritance, the mechanism of transmittance of parental characteristics to offspring. This

1

is the subject of the science of *genetics* or heredity. Here we will be concerned with the physical basis of inheritance and will look into the cell to see how it carries the information needed to duplicate a parental organism and how this information is translated in the course of development into a mature organism.

Having gained a knowledge of the principles of genetics, we shall then examine the interrelationships between genetics, reproduction (with and without sex), and adaptation, for the mode of reproduction of an organism is an aspect of its adaptation. If the environment is very unfavorable, an asexual reproductive system is most effective. But absence of sexuality will affect the ability to recombine character-istics and to evolve with changing conditions. So we must see how organisms have solved the paradox of remaining suited to their im-mediate environment (the "here and now") while at the same time retaining an ability to change or evolve (to adjust to the "there and later"). In this context we shall look at all plants from simple algae or fungi to morphologically complex flowering plants and see how their form, habitat, and mode of reproduction are correlated.

Thus, this book is an effort to look at reproduction in plants from several points of view: how it is done; how it is in harmony with the conditions in which it occurs; and how it, with sexuality, has opened the way to change and increased complexity of form and function.

2

THE NATURE

OF INHERITANCE

PARTICULATE INHERITANCE

If you were asked to explain how organisms transmitted their characteristics to their offspring, you might think up a plausible scheme and be satisfied with that. Or you might get out and contrast parents with their offspring, study family trees or pedigrees, or at least look at existing situations before formulating an explanation. Or maybe you would select an organism with some characteristic that you knew varied, and then would experiment with it by breeding similar and dissimilar kinds. From your observed results you might formulate some laws that you could test by using other organisms and other characters. This last method, known as the experimental method, has come into common use only in the twentieth century and is now taken quite for granted.

In the mid-nineteenth century, however, use of careful experiment was unusual, and those who used it were all the more remarkable. Gregor Mendel was a remarkable man. In 1865 he published the results of eight years of experimenting with plant hybrids. In the course of making artificial hybrids with ornamental plants—he was looking for new color variants—he had been struck with the regularity with which the same form showed up. This led him to experiment with the development of the progeny of the hybrids.

The cultivated pea (*Pisum sativum*) regularly pollinates itself and exists in many varieties. Some have yellow seeds with smooth seed coat, some have green seeds with rough seed coat, some are short and some tall. Many clear-cut and not so clear-cut differences occur. Mendel chose to work with the clear-cut ones. He proceeded as follows:

Two parent plants were crossed reciprocally; that is, pollen from each plant was placed manually on the style of the other after the

3

stamens had been removed. Seed was collected and grown the next year to produce the hybrid, or first filial generation (F_1). The mode of inheritance varied among the characters studied. In the case of size and shape of leaf or hairiness of certain plant parts, the F_1 was intermediate between the two parents. It might be said that the qualities of the parents blended in the offspring. Mendel didn't explore the inheritance of these characters further.

In other cases the characteristic of one parent prevailed or dominated over that of the other. For instance, when a parent grown from rough seed was crossed with one from smooth, the seed formed was always smooth. Smoothness was dominant and roughness recessive. The recessive trait was not expressed in the F_1. It made no difference whether the dominant character belonged to the seed-bearing or pollen-bearing parent; the hybrid F_1 always looked alike.

Mendel took his hybrid F_1 smooth seeds and grew them to maturity. He let the mature plants self-fertilize, as they normally do, and studied their seeds—the embryonic stage of the second filial generation, or F_2. Whereas all the F_1 individuals had looked alike in the seed stage, the F_2 did not. Some were smooth (the dominant character) and some were rough (the recessive trait). Intermediate or blended forms of seeds were never found.

One of the most extraordinary aspects of Mendel's work was its quantitative nature. It would not have sufficed to do a few experiments and get a crude idea of the results. Mendel used large numbers in order to give weight to his evidence. Table 2-1 shows some results.

Table 2-1. *Crosses made by Mendel to study inheritance of roughness and smoothness of seed coat.*

Generation	Appearance of Seed Coat	Numbers Involved
Parental (P)	Smooth and rough	60 pollinations on 15 plants
First filial (F_1)	All smooth	253 individuals
Second filial (F_2)	5474 smooth, 1850 rough	7324 individuals

Ratio of smooth to rough: 2.96 : 1

Mendel performed similar crosses with comparable numbers of plants in order to study the inheritance of six other characters. All of these, too, were cases of simple dominance where one character was suppressed in the F_1, but it was expressed again in the F_2. The ratio of dominant to recessive types in each case was close to 3 : 1.

It is important to note here that Mendel saw the need to obtain average values. On any given plant the proportion of smooth to rough or yellow to green might deviate considerably from 3 : 1, but in the aggregate the proportion approached this value closely. When Mendel raised the *next* generation of peas by letting the F_2 self-pollinate, he found that all recessive parents produced recessive progeny. In other words, they remained constant with regard to the recessive character in question. However, of those F_2 that were dominant (¾ of the F_2), ⅔ produced progeny of both dominant and recessive types in the ratio of 3 : 1, and ⅓ produced only the dominant type. Thus, while the recessive types were pure with regard to the factor controlling the recessive character, the dominant forms were both pure and impure. Some of them (⅓) produced only progeny with the dominant character, and some (⅔) behaved just like the original hybrid F_1's and gave rise to both dominant and recessive forms. The pure lines are called *homozygous* because they produce only one kind of *zygote* upon self-fertilization. The impure ones are called *heterozygous* because they produce different kinds of zygotes. (A zygote is formed by fusion of egg with sperm. It divides, and its derivative cells divide; thus, a multicellular embryo and finally an adult organism develop from it.)

By experimenting with breeding into this next generation, Mendel found that the F_2 ratio of 3 : 1 dominants to recessives could be resolved into the ratio 1 : 2 : 1 for homozygous dominants, heterozygotes, and homozygous recessives, respectively. The zygotes, which develop into embryos within seeds and then plants, must carry two factors, one from each parent. In the initial, pure lines, the zygotes have two identical factors. In the hybrid, two different factors are brought together. Then in later generations these factors segregate and recombine. The diagram in Fig. 2-1 may clarify this process.

The hybrid F_1 produced three different kinds of seed; two of these were homozygous (and resembled the parents) and one was heterozygous (and resembled the hybrid). Instead of saying that there are three different kinds of seed with respect to genetic behavior, we can say there are three distinct *genotypes:* the homozygous dominant genotype SS, the heterozygous genotype Ss, and the homozygous recessive genotype ss. Genotype is a convenient word, for, as you see, the appearance of individuals (*phenotype*) may be the same but their genetic makeup may differ.

Even before Mendel, scientists had found that hybid organisms are, on the whole, intermediate between their parents. For instance, a

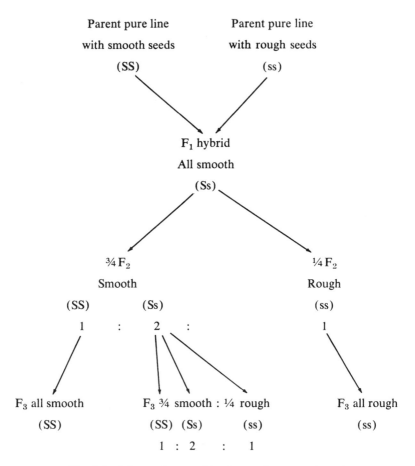

Fig. 2-1. *Scheme for combination and segregation of factors for seed coat. Letters in parentheses represent factors; S = dominant, s = recessive.*

mule is in a general way intermediate between its parents, the donkey and the horse. Mendel found certain characteristics of his plants intermediate—such as shape and hairiness—while others showed dominance. Earlier scientists had also shown that when hybrids self-fertilize, their progeny tend to revert to the parental types. Mendel's results agreed with these observations, for, as you see, by the time the third filial generation is reached, one half of the individuals resemble one or the other parent in specific characteristics. What proportion would resemble the parents in the F_4 or F_5?

The most important point we have seen so far is that development must be controlled by discrete units or particles that retain their identity from generation to generation. This conclusion is inescapable because of absence of blending. This "particulate" inheritance might have been called "atomic," because it presupposes discrete indivisible units that govern development of characters much as matter is made up of discrete units called atoms. The way atoms and molecules do in fact carry the genetic information will be discussed in Chapter 4.

BEHAVIOR OF THE GENE: DOMINANCE AND INCOMPLETE DOMINANCE

It is helpful now to introduce the term *gene*—the name given to the discrete genetic factor that controls development (the molecular structure of genes is discussed in Chapter 5). Mendel emphasized those characters that could exist in only two states; seed coat texture, for instance, can be either smooth or rough. The genes that govern development of these characters exist in two forms: dominant and recessive. His study of hybrids showed that each plant has at least a double dose of genes controlling development of characters. The genes that act on the same character and exist in pairs in the mature plant are called *alleles*. Thus S, which produces smooth seeds, is dominant to its allele s, which results in development of rough seeds. They compose a single gene pair that regulates development of a character. Many such pairs act together in development of the whole organism.

There are instances, however, where dominance is not complete. A German geneticist, Baur, crossed a white-flowered snapdragon with a red-flowered one. The F_1 progeny had pink instead of red or white flowers. But the hereditary material had not actually blended, for when an F_2 was raised, three flower types appeared. Some individuals were red-flowered, some pink-flowered, and some white-flowered. They occurred in the ratio of 1 : 2 : 1 respectively. Here was a striking deviation from dominance, yet at the same time it is a beautiful verification of Mendel's results. In Fig. 2-2, the F_2 shows the two genotypes that carry the "dominant" allele instead of merging them both under the appearance of the dominant form. Compare this case with that of inheritance of seed coat shown in Fig. 2-1.

Perhaps it is safer to say that dominance is a matter of degree. Sometimes the heterozygote is indistinguishable by eye from the homozygous dominant, sometimes it differs slightly from it, and

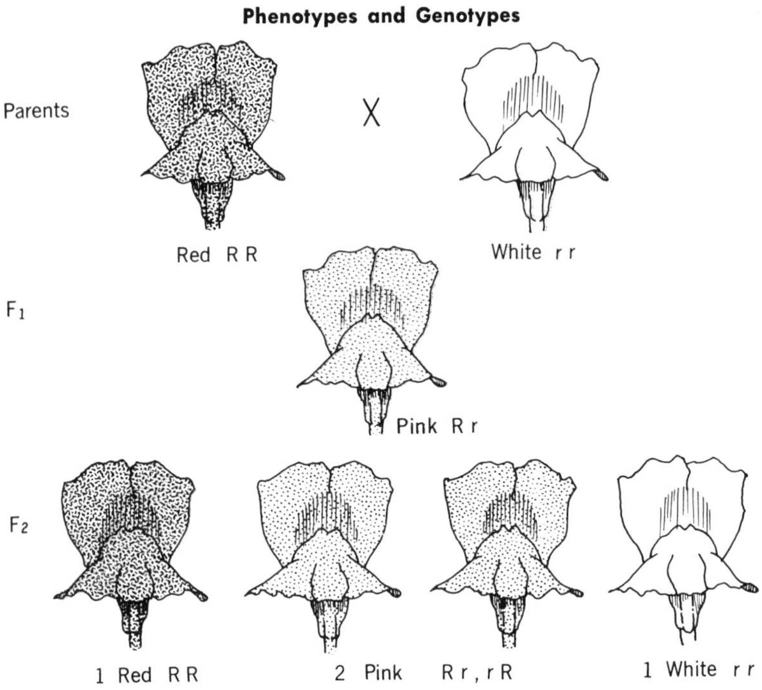

Fig. 2-2. *Incomplete dominance in snapdragon.*

sometimes, as above, it is intermediate between homozygous dominants and recessives. Clearly, a great deal depends on how carefully one looks. Frequently, detailed chemical analyses will reveal differences that the eye cannot see.

BEHAVIOR OF THE GENE: FACTOR INTERACTION

Complementary and Modifying Genes

Just as two alleles in heterozygous condition in snapdragons interact to bring about pink flowers, so can genes of *different* allelic pairs interact. An early instance of factor interaction was analyzed by Bateson, Saunders, and Punnett in 1906. A very puzzling situation had been found in which a hybrid between two white-flowered sweet peas (*Lathyrus odoratus*) had purple flowers. The parents looked similar and produced white progeny when selfed, but together their genetic contributions produced purple flowers! The explanation can be seen in Table 2-2. Three different allelic pairs are at work: C (color factor) is a basic gene needed for any kind of color, and R

Table 2-2. *Complimentary gene action and epistasis as shown in inheritance of flower color in sweet peas. A dash indicates that the phenotype will not be affected regardless of the allele present.*

Phenotypes and Genotypes

Parents	White CC rr BB	×	White cc RR bb
Possible gametes:	C r B		c R b
F_1		All purple Cc Rr Bb	
Possible gametes:	C R B, C R b, C r B, C r b, c R B, c R b, c r B, c r b		

F_2 White - - rr - -   Purple C - R - B -   Red C - R - bb
             cc - - - -

(red factor) is also needed for color. If both dominant C and R are present, red flowers are produced. A dominant B (blue factor) modifies the color to purple. So, the three factors interact to make purple; two complement one another to make color itself possible; a third modifies the expression of the first two. Since B depends on the other genes for its expression, it is said to be *hypostatic* to them; they are *epistatic* to it.

The principal lesson from this experiment is that more than one pair of genes may work together in controlling the development of characters. The expression of one may depend on the activity of another and vice versa, in which case they complement each other. Or the effect of one or several gene pairs may be altered or modified by others present.

Additive Genes and Quantitative Characters

There are great apparent differences in the relative contributions of genes to development of characters. Some genes individually have a large effect, as in the cases investigated by Mendel. In the foregoing blue-flowered sweet pea, three sets of genes cooperated in the development of the final character. In most characteristics concerned with degree of expression (quantitative characters) rather than kind (qualitative characters), many genes work together. Remember size and shape of leaf or hairiness of the pea plant mentioned by Mendel? He couldn't find dominance in their control. The F_1 was intermediate in these characteristics when greatly differing parents were crossed. Such characters are normally under the control of many genes (that is, under polygenic control). The genes interact, each having a small effect alone, and together effecting complete development. Often the effect of each gene is so slight that refined statistical procedures are needed to reveal it. Small wonder that Mendel sought out genes with obvious action.

The first cases of polygenic inheritance were analyzed by Nilsson-Ehle, a Swedish geneticist. One was inheritance of color in grains of wheat. At first there appeared to be continuous, gradual variation in color, from white through pink to deep red. But closer examination showed that there were discrete classes of color: white, pale red, etc. Crossing of pure lines and analysis of segregation in F_2 and F_3 generations revealed three pairs of genes, or six genes altogether, acting on the color character. When all six were dominant, dark red resulted; when all six were recessive, white resulted. Intermediate doses of dominant genes gave intermediate colors. Thus three pairs of genes affected the same character and acted additively.

When three pairs of genes affect a character and have an additive effect, seven different doses of genes are possible. Remember, each parent plant bears two complete sets of genes and transmits to its offspring one set. The makeup of the set is at random, so all possible combinations may arise. Let's treat this case of polygenic inheritance the way Mendel treated his simpler cases—by crossing pure lines and analyzing the hybrid progeny (see Table 2-3). In this case the factors have acted additively; sometimes nonallelic genes even have a multiplicative effect.

In conclusion, we can say that genes behave in many ways: the two members of a gene pair may be related by dominance or incomplete dominance. Separate pairs of genes can also interact additively or even multiplicatively. Qualitative and quantitative characters are not really so different. Qualitative ones are under the control of a few genes, and quantitative ones are under the control of many.

RECOMBINATION

From his first experiments, Mendel learned that inheritance is particulate; it is controlled by genes that separate at the time of formation of germ cells and combine at the time of fertilization. Yet he was not satisfied to know only this. He wanted to know how inheritance of one character was related to that of another. To find out, he crossed a plant having smooth, yellow seeds with one having rough, green seeds. He had already proved that smoothness and yellowness are dominant to roughness and greenness. So it was no surprise that

Table 2-3. *Inheritance of kernel color in wheat (from Nilsson-Ehle).*

Phenotypes and Genotypes

Parents   Darkest red $\dfrac{R_1\ R_2\ R_3}{R_1\ R_2\ R_3}$ ×   White $\dfrac{r_1\ r_2\ r_3}{r_1\ r_2\ r_3}$

Possible gametes: $\underline{R_1\ R_2\ R_3}$ $\underline{r_1\ r_2\ r_3}$

F_1 Medium red $\dfrac{R_1\ R_2\ R_3}{r_1\ r_2\ r_3}$

Possible gametes:

$\underline{R_1R_2R_3}$ $\underline{R_1R_2r_3}$ $\underline{R_1r_2R_3}$ $\underline{R_1r_2r_3}$ $\underline{r_1R_2R_3}$ $\underline{r_1R_2r_3}$ $\underline{r_1R_2r_3}$ $\underline{r_1r_2r_3}$

Dose of R:
   3   2   2   1   2   1   1   0

F_2 (some possible types): $\dfrac{R_1R_2R_3}{R_1R_2R_3}$ $\dfrac{r_1R_2R_3}{R_1r_2r_3}$ $\dfrac{r_1r_2r_3}{R_1r_2r_3}$ $\dfrac{r_1r_2r_3}{r_1r_2r_3}$

Dose of R: 6   3   1   0

Color: Darkest red   Medium red   Palest red   White

all the hybrids (F_1) were smooth and yellow-seeded. The surprise came when he let the F_1 plants self-fertilize: four kinds of seeds appeared in their pods—smooth and yellow (like one parent), rough and green (like the other), and two new types: rough and yellow, and smooth and green. The seed characteristics of the parents had been recombined! Different kinds of plants had been formed.

True to his quantitative methods, Mendel counted the numbers of individuals in each class. The results got by selfing 15 F_1 hybrids are reproduced in Table 2-4. Why such differences in numbers? The answer is best seen by diagramming the possible genotypes of germ cells and mature individuals (see Fig. 2-3). The alleles separate and *assort independently*. This means that the F_1 hybrid is capable of forming germ cells (*gametes*) with four genotypes, as shown in the diagram. Now at fertilization any one of four kinds of eggs fuses with any one of four kinds of sperms to give 16 combinations. This is shown in the Punnett square (named after the British geneticist Punnett) of Fig. 2-3. But look at the genotypes and phenotypes. Nine of them have at least one dominant allele of each pair and therefore resemble the original yellow, smooth-seeded plant; three are homo-

Table 2-4. F_2 *of Mendel's cross between pea plants with smooth, yellow seeds and rough, green seeds.*

Phenotypes	Numbers	Ratio in sixteenths
Smooth & yellow	315	9.1/16
Rough & yellow	101	2.9/16
Smooth & green	108	3.1/16
Rough & green	32	.9/16

zygous recessive (rr) while having a dominant Y and are therefore yellow and rough; three are homozygous recessive (yy) while having dominant R and are therefore green and smooth; while only one in 16 is homozygous recessive and therefore green and rough like the other original parent.

Where factors for two characters assort in this way, four distinct gametes and 16 possible genotypes occur. The kinds and numbers of phenotypes depend on the behavior of genes. If incomplete dominance or factor interaction took place, different ratios of phenotypes would be expected—always, however, based on the existence of these 16 combinations. As an exercise, pretend that one of the two characters is subject to incomplete dominance, as in the snapdragon. How many phenotypes would be found and in what proportions?

The possibilities for new, distinct combinations increase lavishly as the number of independently assorting gene pairs increases. If three independent pairs assort, 27 combinations are possible. In fact, this is what we have seen in the case of polygenic control of grain color of wheat (Table 2-3). If four pairs assort, 16 gametes and 81 different kinds of zygotes can occur, etc. In summary, when there are n allelic pairs assorting, there are 2^n possible gametes and 3^n possible kinds of zygotes.

Recombination is overwhelmingly important just because it makes possible a shuffling of the genetic cards. An astonishingly large number of different hands can be dealt. Some will be winners, some will not, in the game of life. This recombination is interesting to man because it explains his own diversity, and it has practical consequences in plant and animal breeding. By recombining qualities of frost and insect resistance in plants, man has been able to extend their ranges. Very often he has combined desired qualities of one race with those of another to develop new strains.

Phenotypes and Genotypes

Parents   Yellow & smooth $\dfrac{Y\ R}{Y\ R}$ ×   Green & rough $\dfrac{y\ r}{y\ r}$

Possible gametes: Y R   y r

F_1 Yellow & smooth $\dfrac{Y\ R}{y\ r}$

F_2 (look inside the squares)

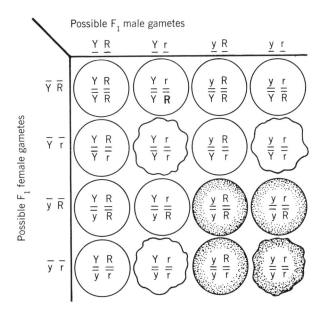

Fig. 2-3. *Diagram of a cross involving two characters governed by two assorting genes.*

MULTIPLE ALLELES

Up to now we have spoken of the allelic pair as being composed of two units (genes) that act together in the zygote and the organism developing from it. From the evidence presented, we have been led to believe that there are only two kinds of genes that can be the partners (alleles) in any pair. These alleles segregate at time of formation of the gametes, each gamete bearing either the one or the other. But there is further evidence with which we must now reckon. A tobacco plant will not normally set seed if pollen from its own flowers is placed on its own styles, because the pollen tubes grow too slowly in the stylar tissue to reach the ovules and fertilize the eggs before the flowers fall. This condition is called *self-incompatibility*. Seed is normally set when the style is dusted with pollen from another plant. Many investigators in Europe and America worked more than 20 years before a satisfactory explanation of the genetic control of incompatibility was found by the Americans East and Mangelsdorf in 1925.

Self-fertilization can be achieved artificially by pollinating the flower when still in bud (thereby giving the pollen more time to grow). Strains of tobacco hybrids were self-fertilized for 12 generations in an effort to get nearly pure lines. The members of these near-pure lines fell into three groups, called X, Y, and Z, each of which was intra-sterile but inter-fertile with members of the other groups. Crosses were made back and forth, i.e., reciprocally, between members of each class, and then the class of the progeny was determined by mating back to the parental stocks. The results are something of a surprise (see Table 2-5).

In the first place, there are three classes. In cases of simple dominance, only two are found. Perhaps incomplete dominance is at play. Yet how can we account for the fact that in the crosses the class of the mother is never represented in the progeny? In Mendel's experiments, reciprocal crosses gave identical hybrids. Not so here. The two other classes appear in roughly the same numbers, reciprocal crosses giving different results. Apparently there is some modification of the simple Mendelian scheme, for the ratio of 1 : 1 is similar to

Table 2-5. *Results of crosses between fertility groups of tobacco (from East and Mangelsdorf, 1925).*

Classes Crossed		Classes Resulting and Number in Each		
Female	Male	X	Y	Z
X	Y		55	47
Y	X	62		46
X	Z		49	50
Z	X	30	28	
Y	Z	68		61
Z	Y	56	40	

what is obtained when a heterozygous F_1 is crossed back to a homozygous recessive parent (called a *test cross;* see Table 2-6). The

Table 2-6. *Diagram of a test cross.*

Genotypes

Parents	AA	×	aa	
Possible gametes:	A		a	
F_1		Aa		
Backcross	F_1 Aa	×	aa	Recessive parent
Possible gametes:	A and a		a	
Progeny	Aa and aa in ratio of 1 : 1			

anomaly is best explained by assuming that there are three alleles involved in the incompatibility reaction, rather than the two we have spoken of in allelic pairs. We can call these S_1, S_2, and S_3. Assume also that pollen tubes cannot grow in styles that bear the same S allele as it does; for example, S_1-bearing pollen cannot grow in S_1S_1, S_1S_2, or S_1S_3 stylar tissue. Letting class X = S_1S_3, class Y = S_1S_2, and class Z = S_2S_3, we can rewrite Table 2-5 (see Table 2-7).

Table 2-7. *Genetic basis for incompatibility in tobacco.*

Classes Crossed, with Genotypes		Classes Resulting, with Genotypes		
Female	Male	X	Y	Z
X S_1S_3	Y S_1S_2		S_1S_2	S_2S_3
Y S_1S_2	X S_1S_3	S_1S_3		S_2S_3
X S_1S_3	Z S_2S_3		S_1S_2	S_2S_3
Z S_2S_3	X S_1S_3	S_1S_3	S_1S_2	
Y S_1S_2	Z S_2S_3	S_1S_3		S_2S_3
Z S_2S_3	Y S_1S_2	S_1S_3	S_1S_2	

This hypothesis fits the observed facts in tobacco and a number of other flowering plants. Further work has shown that there may be many S alleles within a species. These are said to be *multiple alleles.* They are actually fairly common. Man's different blood groups result from differences in alleles governing the development of proteins responsible for blood antigen-antibody reaction. In the fruit fly (*Drosophila*), a number of different alleles control development of eye color. Diversity of alleles could be expected if something should change the properties of a gene. Such changes, called *mutations,* do occur. They will be discussed at greater length in Chapter 4.

THE LOCUS

Genes are the discrete particulate factors that control development. We inferred their existence from their action—the nature of inheritance of morphological and physiological characters. We also inferred that they exist in duplicate in the zygote and organism developing from it, and singly in gametes. We spoke of allelic pairs, but now we see that there may be a multiplicity of alleles available, any individual zygote having just two of them. Thus we need a term to replace "allelic pair"—a term to designate the gene or genes of an allelic series which act in a common physiological process, only two of which can occur in any one zygote. *Locus* is the term used. We can now speak of the incompatibility or S locus and comprehend in the locus all the alleles that may occur. In Chapter 4 the locus will be explained as a site on the chromosome.

3

COMPLICATIONS

OF INHERITANCE

LINKAGE

Three papers were published within a few weeks of each other in 1900 in which the authors—de Vries, Correns, and Tschermak— brought Mendel's remarkable paper back to the attention of the scientific world and confirmed and extended his results. Segregation and *random* recombination were unquestionably facts. In 1906, however, Bateson and Punnett discovered evidence indicating that recombination was not universal. In our discussion of complementary gene action in Chapter 2, we saw that in their cross between white-flowered sweet peas the F_1 was purple-flowered because complementary factors C and R were brought together in it, and a factor B modified the color from red to purple by the addition of blue. The original reason for this particular cross was to study inheritance of pollen shape; the color problem just presented itself by chance, as problems seem to do in scientific research. But what did they learn about inheritance of pollen-grain shape?

One white-flowered parent had round pollen grains; the other, long. The F_1 progeny had purple flowers and long pollen grains; long is therefore dominant to round. In the whole F_2 there are 3 : 1 long-to-round pollen plants with white, red, and purple flowers, as would be expected in a case of simple dominance. But how was pollen shape distributed among the different flower colors? If the factor determining pollen form recombines at random with factors C, R, and B, then we should expect 3 : 1 long-to-round pollen types in each of the color classes. But Bateson and Punnett found a *great excess of longs among the purples* (12 : 1 instead of 3 : 1) and an *excess of rounds among the reds* (3.2 : 1 instead of 1 : 3). The factor for long pollen shape was not inherited independently of that for color. Rather, it was linked with the B gene, and the factor for round pollen was linked with the b gene. Two factors having come from the same parent tended to be inherited together in the subsequent progeny. However, the linkage was not absolute. Long didn't always occur with B, but it occurred with at least a higher frequency than expected of independently recombining genes. Keep this in mind when we discuss crossing-over. The outcome of this famous cross is diagrammed in Fig. 3-1; for the sake of simplicity, however, absolute linkage has

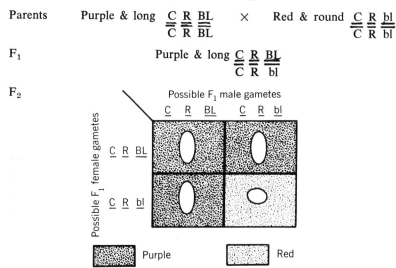

Phenotypes and Genotypes

Parents   Purple & long $\dfrac{C\ R\ BL}{C\ R\ BL}$ ×   Red & round $\dfrac{C\ R\ bl}{C\ R\ bl}$

F_1 Purple & long $\dfrac{C\ R\ BL}{C\ R\ bl}$

F_2

Results of the F_2 cross: 3 : 1 purple-to-red flowers and 3 : 1 long-to-round pollen, but all purple flowers are with long pollen and all red flowers are with round. Thus the characteristics of the parents remain together.

Fig. 3-1. *Linkage illustrated by crossing sweet peas.* (*See also* Fig. 4-4.)

been assumed, and plants have been crossed with purple and red flowers instead of white. Linked genes are symbolized by placing them over a common bar: BL (blue, long), bl (red, round). Unlinked genes are over separate bars.

Linkage remained a perplexing phenomenon until T. H. Morgan and his fellow workers at Columbia University began working with the fruit fly (*Drosophila*). You may know the little fly already; he rises in clouds from over-ripe fruit left in the kitchen or garbage can during summer and autumn. The animal is small and reproduces very quickly. Between 1910 and 1915 Morgan's group was able to study inheritance of more than 100 of its characters. In Morgan's words, "It became evident very soon that these characteristics are inherited in groups." There is one great group of characters that are sex-linked, two other groups slightly greater in number, and finally a fourth group very small in number. So there are four linkage groups in the fruit fly.

SEX LINKAGE

What is meant by the expression *sex-linked?* Sex is a character, or better, a complex of characters, in the same way that flower color or seed smoothness is. Morphological and physiological sexual differences are associated with differences in gametes or sex cells formed by individuals. Female individuals produce eggs; males produce sperm. The sexes may be differently constructed for copulation. And there may be further, less essential differences; for example, the female may be morphologically equipped to protect and nourish the young, and the male may be elaborately ornamented. These are secondary though nevertheless necessary components of over-all sexual difference. By sex linkage we mean inheritance of bodily characters having no functional relevance to sex along with the usual sexual characters. Let's examine a case of sex-linked inheritance that the Columbia school found in the fruit fly.

Red is the usual eye color in the fly. It is called *wild type* because it is normally found in natural, wild individuals. White-eyed flies are occasionally found. If a white-eyed male is mated with a red-eyed female (homozygous for red eyes), male and female F_1 progeny all have red eyes. If the F_1 males and females are then interbred, the resulting F_2 will be 3 : 1 red-to-white-eyed flies. Evidently red is dominant to white. But, lo, the white-eyed flies are all male! Color of eye is linked with sex determination, just as pollen shape was linked with the B locus in sweet peas. Here, too, the factors coming from one parent tend to remain together with the result that maleness is linked with white eyes. We will return to sex linkage when we take up the topics of sex determination and sex chromosomes.

Several anomalies in man are known to be caused by genes linked with those determining sex. Probably the most familiar are colorblindness and hemophilia (bleeding disease in which the affected person's blood does not clot normally).

RECOMBINATION WITHIN LINKAGE GROUPS

In Fig. 3-1, linkage between dominant B and L and recessive b and l factors was represented as absolute: no purple flowers appeared with round pollen, no red flowers with long. But Bateson and Punnett actually found one purple round to every 12 purple longs. There was thus a low frequency of recombination of 7.7 per cent. Similarly, some longs did appear among the reds. This recombination between linked genes was studied extensively by Morgan. The wild type of fly that he studied had a gray body (B) and long wings (V). This type was crossed with a fly with recessive characters: black body (b) and vestigial wings (v). These are linked in the second linkage group. If the linkage is complete, a test cross of the F₁ back to the recessive parent will yield only the parental combinations, but if B recombines with v, and b with V, two new recombinant types will appear. This does happen to the extent shown in Fig. 3-2, which is slightly more than the frequency of recombination between the B and L loci of sweet peas.

When the cross is made between *gray vestigial* and *black long* flies, the frequency of recombination is the same as in the cross between *gray long* and *black vestigial* flies. This shows that the frequency of recombination is independent of the particular association of alleles. Instead it depends on the particular loci compared. In general, recombination between linked genes occurs in definite frequencies. For this reason it is possible to put the loci of a linkage group in a linear sequence by studying the extent of linkage between them. For example, if A locus recombines with B 5 per cent of the time and with C 8 per cent of the time, and B with C 13 per cent, then the sequence must be B − A -- C. By playing the loci off against one another, it has been possible to derive maps of the linkage groups of a number of plants and animals, where "distance" is measured in terms of recombination frequency.

Only two linked characters were studied in the examples from sweet peas and fruit flies. Consider now three linked loci and a cross of ABC by abc. What are the possible genotypes in the test cross of the hybrid to the recessive parent (1) with no recombination, (2) with recombination between A and BC, (3) with recombination between C and AB, and (4) with recombination twice, between A

Phenotypes and Genotypes

Parents

Male
Black, vestigial $\dfrac{bv}{bv}$

Female
Gray, long $\dfrac{BV}{BV}$

F_1

Gray, long $\dfrac{BV}{bv}$

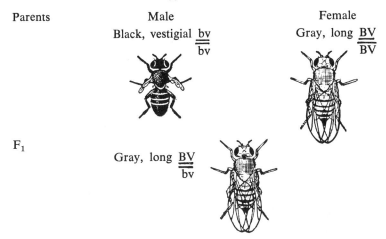

Backcross of F_1 female to black, vestigial male:

	Possible male gametes				Frequency in F_2	
	$\underline{bv}$					
$\underline{BV}$	$\dfrac{BV}{bv}$	gray, long	No crossover	41.5	}	83%
$\underline{bv}$	$\dfrac{bv}{bv}$	Black, vestigial	No crossover	41.5		
$\underline{Bv}$	$\dfrac{Bv}{bv}$	Gray, vestigial	Crossover	8.5	}	17%
$\underline{bV}$	$\dfrac{bV}{bv}$	Black, long	Crossover	8.5		

(Possible female gametes)

Fig. 3-2. *Phenotypes and genotypes of crossover and noncrossover types in fruit flies.*

(*Adapted from T. H. Morgan et al.,* The Mechanism of Mendelian Heredity. *New York: Henry Holt and Company, 1915.*)

and B and between B and C (see Table 3-1)? This is a hypothetical case, but in fact it does happen just this way in nature.

Table 3-1. *Hypothetical case of single and double recombinations between linked characters.*

Parents	$\underline{\underline{\text{ABC}}}$	×	$\underline{\underline{\text{abc}}}$
	ABC		abc

F_1 $\underline{\underline{\text{ABC}}}$
                             abc

Possible gametes from F_1:

Recombinations		Gametes
0	$\dfrac{\text{ABC}}{\text{abc}}$	<u>ABC</u> and <u>abc</u>
1	ABC / abc	<u>Abc</u> and <u>aBC</u>
1	ABC / abc	<u>ABc</u> and <u>abC</u>
2	ABC / abc	<u>aBc</u> and <u>AbC</u>

The cause of recombination within linkage groups has been called *crossing-over* by Morgan, and today we often speak loosely of both the cause and the effect as crossing-over. Its occurrence is not universal. Female fruit flies have it but males don't; some species have a higher incidence than others. Also, a crossover in one place may inhibit crossovers in the immediate neighborhood. Crossing-over is under genetic control just like other morphological and physiological characters, and it has adaptive and evolutionary significance that will be discussed later.

In calling the recombination within linkage groups "crossing-over" we have subtly changed our field of discourse. We were talking about effects, and now we are talking of causes. What about causes, anyway? What causes segregation, recombination, linkage, and recombination within linkage groups? What are the physical bases of these remarkable effects? These are the main questions for the next chapter.

4

HEREDITARY

MATTER:

THE CHROMOSOME

Increases in depth and breadth of knowledge have resulted from the observation of effects or behavior, at one level, to a search for causes at another. Through breeding experiments using whole organisms, it has been possible to develop laws of inheritance. The causes for these laws must be looked for in the physical makeup of the organism itself, in its cells and molecules. In other words we must shift our level of inquiry from the organism to the cell and its components.

Actually, in using the term *locus* in Chapter 2 we got ahead of ourselves, for "locus" is Latin for "place," and its use connotes spatiality, whereas we have not really "placed" anything by way of assigning causes to certain substances in certain places. Also, as noted earlier, we shifted levels by introducing the term "crossing-over," because "crossing-over" refers to a chromosomal event that is thought to cause recombination within linkage groups.

Development of the science of genetics has proceeded from study at both levels. Even Mendel, in his famous original paper of 1865, showed awareness of the fact that inheritance is governed by factors carried in the eggs and pollen of his pea plants. But for the most part, the study of cytology went on independently of genetics until early in the twentieth century.

THE CELL

By the turn of the last century, a great deal was known about cells and their behavior in the course of development. Aided by microscopy, man had learned that all organisms are cellular and begin life

23

as single cells. Usually these cells had begun as large sedentary eggs, which later had fused with small motile sperm.

Every cell was found to have inside it a kernel-like body called the *nucleus*. These nuclei could be stained with dyes, and at certain stages the stain was taken up in them by thread-like structures subsequently called *chromosomes* (from the Greek: *chrome* = color + *some* = body). Each organism was shown to have a constant and characteristic endowment of chromosomes in its cells. *Trillium*, or wake-robin, has ten easily observed chromosomes that display a spiraled structure; many fungi have chromosomes that look like mere specks when seen through a high-powered light microscope. The number and form of the chromosomes was shown to be, with some exceptions, the same in all the cells of an organism; and only rarely were cells found without a nucleus and chromosomes. Red blood cells in man and sieve-tube elements in angiosperm plants lack nuclei, but they play special physiological roles and have a limited life-span.

There was at this time much discussion about whether the chromosomes were persistent structures or were formed anew at every cell division. The controversy was provoked by the fact that in most cells the chromosomes are evident at only certain stages of cell division; when the cells are not dividing, the chromosomes appear to lose their identities. However, some organisms were found in which the chromosomes persisted in a diffuse condition between cell divisions and emerged in early division disposed in the same manner as at the end of the previous division. The experimental work of the German biologist Boveri, especially, established the individuality and genetic continuity of chromosomes. At present so much evidence has accumulated that no one questions the conclusion that chromosomes have integrity throughout the life of cells and an ability to duplicate themselves with extraordinary exactness. The behavior and chemical makeup of chromosomes is the subject of this and the next chapter.

By the turn of the last century it was also known that eggs and sperms always carry one complete complement or set of chromosomes —for which reason they are termed haploid (*haplo* = one + *id* = set). The fertilized egg, or zygote, carries the combined two sets and is therefore called diploid (*diplo* = double). In the zygote and all cells derived from it, half of the chromosomes are from the mother and half from the father.

Suppose now that you are back in the first years of this century. Mendel's paper has just been brought to the attention of the scientific world after having gone unappreciated for 35 years. Its dis-coverers—Correns, Tschermak, and de Vries—and a host of other biologists have seized upon it, rapidly corroborated its contents, and greatly added to them. Ask yourself: How does this zygote know how to become a horse instead of a horse chestnut? Or more soberly: What physical explanation can I propose to explain the facts that (1) inheritance is particulate; (2) genes occur in pairs that preserve their identity in the zygote and segregate at the time of formation of gametes; (3) genes, which govern development of characters, can recombine (characters can be recombined); (4) genes may be linked; and (5) recombination may occur in differing degrees within linkage groups? What sort of system can explain these facts and assure that each individual receives a complete and proper dose of information-bearing genes? It must operate at the time of gamete formation, for this is when gene distribution takes place.

Gametes are simply rather specialized cells derived from pre-exist-ing cells by cell division. If the genes were drifting around inside the cell individually in unordered arrangement, at the time of division both alleles of a pair might go to the same daughter cell and leave the other deficient (see Case I of Fig. 4-1). But if each complement of genes were gathered into a bag and the bags separated at gamete formation, each daughter cell would be assured of a full set of genes. Yet, if this were so, recombination would be impossible; all genes from each parent would be linked together (Case II of Fig. 4-1).

To get around this problem we can suppose that genes line up in two sets, each gene facing its counterpart allele, and that chance alone dictates the set that a particular allele joins. Then when these two sets separate into daughter cells, each cell will receive a full set of genes and recombination will have been possible (Case III of Fig. 4-1). "All right," you say, "but what about linkage?" It isn't provided for. To do so we must place the genes together in groups, and, if we permit groups to exchange parts occasionally, we will have provided for linkage and crossing-over as well. This (Case IV of Fig. 4-1) is a compromise between complete linkage of Case II and complete recombination of Case III, and as a *compromise* it is very important and will be returned to in a later chapter.

This was the kind of deductive approach that led biologists to con-clude that chromosomes are the carriers of the genes, for chromo-somes form a system that just fits Case IV. The "chromosome theory of inheritance" has now been proved in so many ways it is no longer referred to as a theory at all but simply accepted as fact.

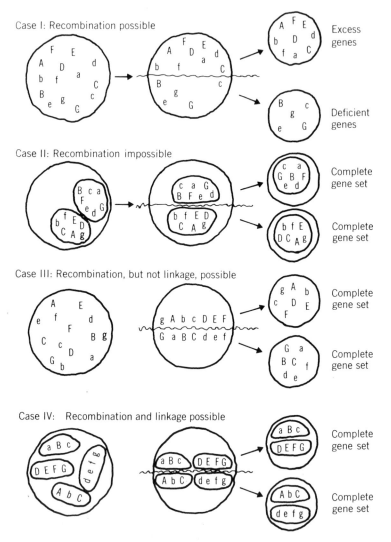

Fig. 4-1. *Proposed arrangements of genes in cells—before, during, and after division.*

MITOSIS

If you were to place a single-celled protozoan or alga in suitable conditions, it would grow and divide, and eventually you would have an incredible number of cells. Each would look just like the other. You would never be able to observe recombination or any other genetic phenomenon discussed so far. The same would happen if you grew bulbils from a lily or gladiolus or propagated cuttings from a favored apple tree. Each individual grown from such bulbils or shoots would look much like the others when grown under similar conditions, because the cells involved increase by what are called *mitotic divisions*. They occur in ordinary growth of embryonic cells after fertilization of an egg, at the shoot and root tips of plants, and in the protozoan and algal cultures. They do not normally permit recombination, segregation, and crossing-over; these phenomena arise as a result of another kind of cell division, called *meiosis*, which precedes gamete formation. We will discuss mitosis first.

With a phase-contrast microscope and time-lapse motion picture camera, we can record the behavior of chromosomes during mitotic cell divisions. Inside a clear nucleus, long threads appear as if by magic. By twisting and coiling, they shorten and thicken and assume the somewhat rope-like appearance of chromosomes. The chromosomes then migrate to a plane at the center of the cell; some are held to the plane at their centers, others nearer their ends. In fact, they appear to be pulled or pushed to it by fibers which radiate from two poles that have this plane as their equator. A fiber is attached to each chromosome at a particular site called a *kinetochore* (*centromere*). The arms of the chromosome on each side of the kinetochore may dangle away from the equator.

Although the chromosomes appear at a glance to be simple, careful examination reveals that they are really duplicate structures. The identical twin-like threads are called *chromatids*. A new exact copy of each chromosome was formed before cell division began and was closely intertwined with the original. Now the chromatids move to different poles, kinetochore foremost, with arms dangling behind. Having neared the poles, they uncoil, elongate, and dissolve from view. The body of the cell, the *cytoplasm,* becomes divided by furrowing or cell-plate formation in the region of the former equatorial plane. Thus two daughter cells result, each with a full complement of chromosomes.

The principle elements of mitosis are the duplicated chromosomes, which carry the genetic material, and the mitotic apparatus. This apparatus is composed of protein fibers oriented between two poles. Some fibers run from pole to pole and form a spindle-shaped figure (the central spindle) widest at the equator and narrowest at the poles.

Others run from pole to kinetochores; they are the chromosome fibers. The importance of the kinetochores is shown by the fact that when they are lost or destroyed (as by ionizing radiation) the chromosome will not come to lie in the equatorial plane or be moved back toward the pole.

The intriguing questions of how the mitotic apparatus is built and how it functions are being actively pursued by scientists today. (See the article by D. Mazia cited in the references at the end of this book.)

The whole mitotic process is diagrammed in Fig. 4-2. For convenience it has been divided into stages and these have been given their technical names. Careful study of this diagram will help you visualize this fabulous process. But remember that it is a continuous process; the stages are simply designated for convenience. During *interphase* the cell is far from inactive; it is busy metabolizing and synthesizing

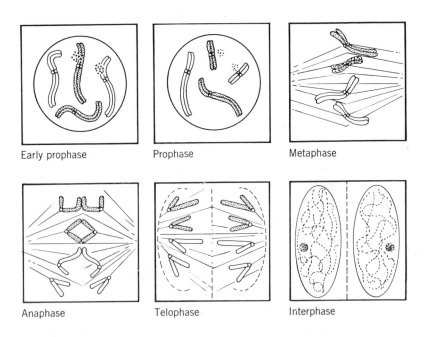

Early prophase   Prophase   Metaphase

Anaphase   Telophase   Interphase

Fig. 4-2. *Stages of mitosis.*

new materials, preparing for self-duplication by synthesizing new chromatids. In *prophase* the duplicated chromosomes, each composed of two chromatids, shorten by coiling and the nucleolus and nuclear membrane disappear. The central spindle forms and chromosomal fibers join poles to kinetochores; the paired chromatids move to the equatorial plane. During *metaphase* the chromosomes are held in the equatorial plane. At *anaphase* the sister chromatids are separated and moved poleward. During *telophase* they uncoil and return to invisibility; nucleolus and nuclear membrane are reconstituted, and *cytokinesis*—division of cell body—occurs. So each daughter cell receives a full set of chromosomes, and, given that the genes are in the chromosomes, each cell has the same genetic complement.

MEIOSIS

Mitosis is an *equational* division because it produces daughter cells whose genomes are identical to each other's and to the parent cell's. Meiosis, on the other hand, is *differential* because the number of chromosomes in daughter cells resulting from it is half that of the parent cell, and also because the daughter cells differ qualitatively in their chromosomal makeup. The mechanism of the division, however, resembles mitosis with the signal difference that in the initial prophase the chromosomes from one parent become aligned with their respective mates (called homologues) from the other parent. (This alignment is so important that it is given a special name, *synapsis*). The synapsed homologues then move to the center of the spindle. However, their kinetochores appear to repel one another and don't come to lie in the equatorial plane. One of the homologues goes to one pole and the other to the other. Thus the sister chromatids in the duplicated chromosomes stay together, or, to look at it a little differently, sister kinetochores don't separate although those of the homologues do. In this way synapsis entails a reduction from the diploid to the haploid number while ensuring that each daughter cell receives a full complement of genes. It also makes recombination possible, because chance alone dictates whether one or the other of a pair of duplicated homologues is oriented to a given pole. If, for example, the diploid chromosome number of an organism is four, there are two sets of homologous chromosomes, each set of two contributed by maternal egg and paternal sperm. When the two pairs of synapsed homologues come to the equatorial plane, the two paternal chromosomes may be oriented toward the same pole. If they are, the genome of cells arising from them will resemble that of paternal sperm (except for differences introduced by crossing-over, which are discussed below). If the paternal chromosomes are oriented to different poles, a new combination of chromosomes will be created in the haploid cells formed: one paternal and one maternal chromosome. The chromosomes that move apart after this first division are already duplicated. There follows now a second simple mitotic division in which the kinetochores of the duplicated chromosomes come to lie in the equatorial plane and the sister chromatids are separated as each is moved poleward by its own kinetochore. Sister kinetochores thus separate in this second division. Here we see another basic difference between mitosis and meiosis: in mitosis the products of duplication are immediately separated by spindle activity; in meiosis two successive nuclear divisions occur before the duplicated kinetochores are separated. These two divisions are called meiosis I and meiosis II.

The time of duplication of meiotic chromosomes is not definitely known and is still being actively studied. However, it probably begins in interphase and is completed by the end of the pachytene stage of prophase of the first division.

The basic course of meiosis in plants and animals is outlined in Fig. 4-3. For convenience, the events of prophase I have been separated into stages. The arbitrariness of the stages is exemplified by the fact that sometimes the various chromosomes of a nucleus may be in slightly different stages at the same time.

Meiosis I

Prophase I

Leptotene: the attenuated chromosomes become visible as simple strands, not clearly composed of two chromatids.

Zygotene: the homologous chromosomes synapse zipper-fashion, kinetochore to kinetochore, gene to gene, end to end. Characteristic features such as nucleolar-organizing regions or constrictions are matched up.

Pachytene: the chromosomes continue to shorten and thicken and coil around one another.

Diplotene: the chromosomes appear to have duplicated; each homologue is now composed of two sister chromatids. The homologues appear to repel each other but are held together at one or more places along their lengths. These places are called *chiasmata* (singular: *chiasma*) and come about because the sister chromatids get "divorced" and pair up with one of the chromatids from the

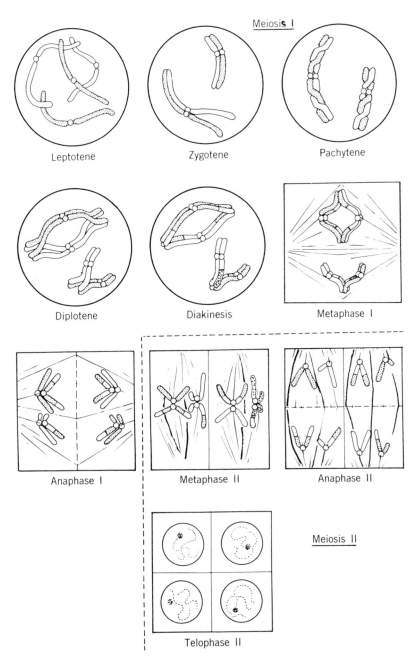

Meiosis I

Leptotene   Zygotene   Pachytene

Diplotene   Diakinesis   Metaphase I

Anaphase I   Metaphase II   Anaphase II

Meiosis II

Telophase II

Fig. 4-3. *Stages of meiosis.*

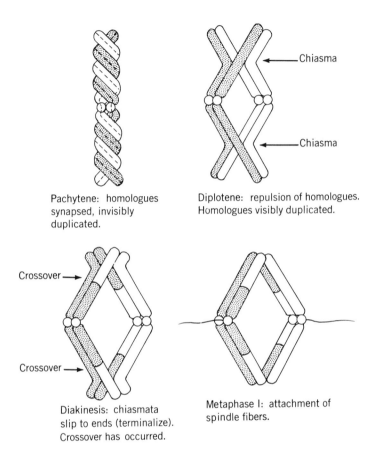

Pachytene: homologues synapsed, invisibly duplicated.

Diplotene: repulsion of homologues. Homologues visibly duplicated.

Diakinesis: chiasmata slip to ends (terminalize). Crossover has occurred.

Metaphase I: attachment of spindle fibers.

Fig. 4-4. *Crossing-over in detail.*

other homologue (see Fig. 4-4). This results in a crisscross arrangement. If the chromatids did not change pairing partners in this way, the homologues would become separated.

Diakinesis: coiling continues, and the chromosomes continue to shorten and thicken. The chromatids that have crisscrossed and changed partners slip past each other and cause the chiasmata to move toward the ends of the chromosome arms.

Metaphase I: synapsed homologues move to the center of the spindle, but the kinetochores, repelling one another, lie to each side of the equatorial plane and equidistant from it.

Anaphase I: attraction between chromatids ceases, which allows homologues to move apart toward the poles. They do so under the influence of spindle fibers and kinetochores.

Telophase I: the chromosomes of each haploid set may enter a telophase condition or they may retain their coiled, shortened form and enter immediately into meiosis II.

Meiosis II: In this essentially mitotic division, the kinetochores lie in the metaphase plane, and kinetochores of sister chromatids instead of those of homologues (as in meiosis I) separate at anaphase. Meiosis II differs from an ordinary mitosis in that sister chromatids are not closely intertwined. Rather, they remain in the dissociated condition they assumed in anaphase I.

Meiosis I is reductional and differential, for reduction in number and formation of different or new combinations of chromosomes occurs. Meiosis II is equational because daughter cells are formed with chromosome number equal to that of the parent nucleus, but it too may be differential in that the genomes resulting from it may be different. The phenomenon of crossing-over explains how this can be.

CROSSING-OVER

During zygotene and pachytene, the homologous chromosomes are intimately associated and coiled around each other (see Figs. 4-3 and 4-4). At diplotene they repel one another but are held together at certain points (*chiasmata*) where the chromatids change pairing mates. It is not clear how chiasmata are formed, but combined cytological and genetic studies have shown that at the site of each there is a physical exchange of chromatid material between homologues. This exchange is called crossing-over; it causes recombination within linkage groups, which was discussed in Chapter 3.

Chiasma formation may be restricted to certain places on a chromosome, or it may be more or less at random. In general, large chromosomes are likely to have more numerous chiasmata, because crossing-over cannot occur within the confines of a certain least length of chromosome. It follows also that the farther apart genes are located on a chromosome, the more likely they are to be recombined by crossing-over. Single, double, or even triple crossovers may occur, and at each one they may involve any two of the four chromatids.

Meiosis II is a differential division because each nucleus formed can receive a slightly different combination of genes. The sister chromatids that separate at anaphase II are no longer identical after crossing-over has taken place. It is equational only in that the *number* of chromosomes of its daughter nuclei equals that of the nucleus at the end of anaphase I.

Chromosomal behavior in mitosis and meiosis is a physical parallel of the conceptual scheme deduced from analysis of inheritance of characters. Chromosomes fit Case IV of Fig. 4-1 very nicely. First, they preserve their identity from fertilization to meiosis, and they are unitary. Second, each haploid gamete receives a representative of each homologous pair. Third, since there are hundreds of genes and many fewer chromosomes, the genes must be linked in groups on them. Fourth, crossing-over occurs, and furthermore the farther apart genes are on chromosomes, the more likely they are to recombine by crossing-over. This explains the existence of differences in frequency of recombination between genes within one linkage group. So it appears that genes are arranged in linear sequence in chromosomes. It took years of research to discover this physical basis of inheritance. Today no one questions that chromosomes do bear the hereditary material, but one may still reasonably question how many factors are borne in the cytoplasm. If recombination is never observed for a certain character, there is no way of knowing where the genes determining it are borne. In fact, much of what is essential to life is inherited in the cytoplasm: cell membranes, and organelles such as mitochondria and plastids. It isn't the chromosomes alone that are inherited.

One other point about meiosis and mitosis: meiosis is a mechanism for reducing chromosome number to the haploid level before syngamy (fertilization). If reduction did not take place, the number would double every generation. That obviously could not go on for long. Yet it does happen to a limited degree, and chromosomes do other strange things that have genetic consequences. The study of the genetic consequences of chromosomal behavior is known as cytogenetics. It was born, as a science, of the marriage of genetics and cytology around 1915. Let's look at some of its discoveries.

PHENOMENA AT THE CHROMOSOMAL LEVEL

Chromosome Number and Polyploidy

An important advance was made by cytogeneticists when they found that the number of linkage groups was equal to the number of pairs of homologues—that is, the haploid number. In *Drosophila* there were four chromosomes in egg and sperm; eight in the adult fly. The garden pea was found to have a haploid number of seven by Sansome in 1933. Isn't it remarkable, then, that Mendel chose to discuss just seven pairs of characters? He had probably observed linkage but didn't want to mention it. It would have made his findings all the more incredible. Counts have shown that animals and plants may have from two to hundreds of chromosomes. What a range and what different amounts of linkage result!

The member species of some genera and families all have the same number: all pines, for instance, have a haploid number of 12. In other cases the chromosome numbers of related species may be multiples of a common base number. In the genus of the wheats, *Triticum,* the base number is seven. *T. monococcum* and *T. (Aegilops) speltoides* are diploid with $2 \times 7 = 14$. *T. durum* and *T. dicoccoides* are tetraploid with $4 \times 7 = 28$. *T. vulgare* and *T. spelta* are hexaploid with $6 \times 7 = 42$. And finally, plant breeders have created some that are octaploid with $8 \times 7 = 56$ chromosomes. This phenomenon is called *polyploidy*. It has several causes: sometimes in vegetative cells a mitotic nuclear division may occur, but cell division does not take place. The two daughter nuclei may then fuse with the result that the cell has twice its normal chromosome number. This may be brought about by treatment with temperatures or chemicals. Nowadays it is possible to create polyploids at will. You may have seen super polyploid snapdragons in nurseries.

Even more rarely, two diploid gametes will fuse to form a tetraploid. The probability of their fusing will be the product of the probabilities of their being formed. For example, if the probability of occurrence of an unreduced sperm is one in a thousand, and that of an egg is the same, the probability that the two v.ll fuse is one in a million. This process has accelerated evolution in wheat and several other important plant groups, because it has made possible the bringing together of qualities otherwise not recombinable. For example, assume that species A has some desirable trait and species B some other. It may be possible to cross the species, but the hybrid formed is sterile because the chromosomes of A and B will not synapse in meiosis. Failure of synapsis results in some daughter cells' getting too many and others' getting too few chromosomes or, in other words, abnormal chromosome complements. The gametes formed from these cells may themselves die or the zygote they produce dies; thus sterility results. When, however, the entire chromosome complement of each species is present in the hybrid (as happens in fusion of diploid gametes), the chromosomes of A will synapse among themselves, and B chromosomes will do likewise. Each gamete has a set of both A and B chromosomes. The tetraploid is then fertile and the qualities of the two species have been brought together. This is what has happened in wheat (Table 4-1).

Table 4-1. *Evolution of wheats through allopolyploidy.*

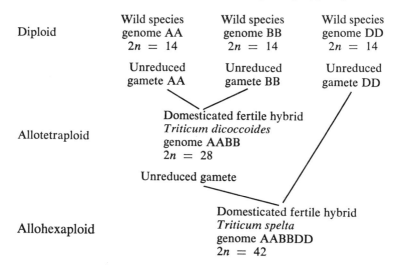

When the polyploid arises from two different species, it is called an *allopolyploid;* when from the doubling of the chromosomes of just one species, an *autopolyploid.* An example of this may be found in the potato, *Solanum tuberosum,* where plants with 48 and 96 chromosomes have both been found; the principal cultivated potato is an autotetraploid.

Earlier, in the passage on additive genes and quantitative characters, we learned that Nilsson-Ehle found three pairs of genes to be controlling grain color in *Triticum vulgare.* When all six genes were dominant, deep red grains resulted; when all six were recessive, white grains developed. Intermediate doses gave intermediate colors. Now we know that there are three genomes in *T. vulgare.* Apparently each genome has contributed alleles affecting grain color, and so in this case we can explain inheritance partly in terms of the chromosome complement. This is an interesting example, because it shows that the polyploid is endowed with a larger inherent source of variation than the diploid.

Inversions and Translocations

Homologues exchange parts in crossing-over, and in this way new combinations of genes are created within chromosomes, while the sequence of genes remains the same. Sometimes, however, chromosomes break and reconstitute themselves in a new order, causing what are known as *inversions*. These can be detected at the time of pairing of homologues in the prophase of meiosis I (see Fig. 4-5),

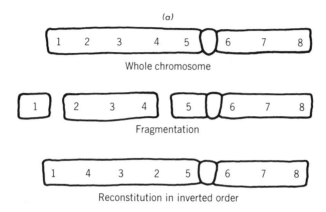

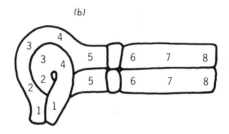

Fig. 4-5. (*a*) *Fragmentation and reconstitution with inversion of a segment.* (*b*) *Pairing of inverted chromosome with normal form.*

because, if the paternal chromosome has a different order than its maternal homologue, the homologues will not become juxtaposed like straight ribbons—a loop will have to be formed.

The presence of a loop reduces crossing-over within its region, with the result that the inverted segment of chromosome becomes inherited as a block of genes. Thus, inversion can be a mechanism favoring coherence of genetic factors.

The mechanism (or mechanisms) whereby inversions reduce crossing-over is complicated and still a subject of investigation. Some evidence indicates that the loop itself reduces crossing-over, perhaps by impairing synapsis. In the main, however, the reduction seems to come about by elimination of the chromatids that experience crossing-over. This will happen because, when a single crossover occurs between chromatids within a loop, two chromatids with kinetochores become joined together and a fragment without kinetochore is formed from their distal segments. The fragment and chromosomal bridge formed between the centromeres at anaphase are usually left out of the daughter nuclei. Thus, only noncrossover chromatids form viable

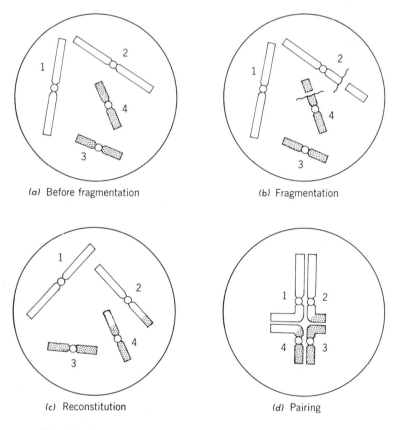

    (a) Before fragmentation   (b) Fragmentation

    (c) Reconstitution   (d) Pairing

Fig. 4-6. *Fragmentation and reconstitution with translocation of a segment.*

gametes, and, at the price of some genetic death, the original blocks of genes are preserved intact. The phrase *genetic death* is used here because it is death brought on by the intrinsic genetic mechanism, not by extrinsic causes. *Translocation* is an exchange of material between nonhomologous chromosomes. It, too, can be detected at the prophase of meiosis I, for if the maternal and paternal chromosomes differ with respect to the translocation, pairing will have to occur between more than one pair of homologues (see Fig. 4-6).

You can readily see that if chromosomes 1 and 2 go to one pole and 3 and 4 go to another, the daughter cells will be deficient in chromosomal material and death of the cells or their derivatives may result. If, rather, 1 and 4 and 2 and 3 accompany each other, the whole genome will be represented in each daughter cell. Translocation causes recombination of genetic material between chromosomes and also results in reduced crossing-over. In fact, in some evening primroses it has led to the plant's 14 chromosomes' being divided into two groups, which in effect act as two large linkage groups. Outcrossing cannot occur in these same plants because they self-pollinate, and lethal genes have been incorporated into the genome in such a way that the two linkage groups are preserved intact. Recombination is greatly reduced.

Deficiencies and Duplications

Fragmentation and rejoining of chromosomes can also cause deficiencies and duplications of chromosomal material. Furthermore, chromosomes may fuse together. We saw in wheat how chromosome number might increase in even multiples; now through fragmentation and fusion we find an explanation for changes in number in uneven multiples. The species of *sedges* (genus *Carex*) offer a good illustration of this:

	haploid number
C. *pilulifera*	9
C. *ericetorum*	15
C. *panicea*	16
C. *humilis*	18
C. *montana*	19
C. *depauperata*	22
C. *wahuensis*	24
C. *bicolor*	25
C. *dioica*	26
C. *frigida*	28
C. *lachenalii*	29

This brief discussion of chromosomal phenomena makes it evident that chromosomes are not static structures at all and genomes of organisms can change and evolve even without changes in the genes themselves. The peculiarities of chromosome behavior have great significance to recombination and linkage and thereby to adaptation and evolution of populations. But the enquiring mind has probably already jumped to the next level of investigation: the subchromosomal. What are genes, and how do they act and interact in development? The search for answers to these questions has carried genetics to the molecular level, and much of what is called molecular biology today owes its inception to the asking of these very questions. We can do little more here than summarize very briefly some of the most remarkable discoveries and suggest to the reader that he refer to a text devoted more exclusively to the topic of physico-chemical mechanisms of heredity and development.

5

HEREDITARY MATTER:

INHERITANCE AND

DEVELOPMENT—

THE GENE

"The gene, like the Roman God Janus, has two faces, one turned toward the maintenance of its own integrity, one looking toward the synthetic metabolism of the cell" (Schulz, 1941).

The gene has two main functions: to duplicate itself prior to cell division, and to control the synthetic processes involved in metabolism and differentiation. As if this were not enough, it is also capable of permanent change called mutation. In seeking to discover what a gene is, investigators have explored these various properties. Let us do so too.

CHROMOSOMES AND GENES

Makeup of Chromosomes

If genes are in the chromosomes, perhaps we can tell what they are made of by finding out what chromosomes are made of. Miescher, a German scientist active in the last quarter of the nineteenth century, did a chemical analysis of nuclei of fish sperm. He found that they were composed principally of nucleic acids (which will be discussed more fully below) and histone and protamine proteins. By 1930 it had been discovered that nucleic acids are of two kinds: ribose nucleic acid (RNA) and deoxyribose nucleic acid (DNA), the two being similar in over-all structure but differing in one of their components. They also react differently to stains, and this made it possible to note that DNA is principally in the chromosomes and RNA mainly in the nucleolus and cytoplasm. Histones and protamines are found almost exclusively in chromosomes.

Caspersson took advantage of the fact that nucleic acids have a characteristic absorption spectrum. That is to say, they absorb electromagnetic radiation in a characteristic way, absorbing most effectively in the ultraviolet region of the spectrum. He developed a microscope with which to study the amounts of nucleic acid in the cell and even inside the chromosomes. He located the DNA in the parts of the chromosomes that take up stain. These regions had already been shown to be where the genes mostly lie. Apparently histones and protamines form the structural backbone of the chromosome, and DNA is localized along the backbone. But direct evidence revealing the component that is genetically active was not obtained until 1943, when Avery, McLeod, and McCarty performed an experiment described below.

Pneumococcus, the bacterium that causes pneumonia, exists in two forms. One (called R for rough) lacks a polysaccharide capsule around its cells and is not virulent; another (called S for smooth) has such a capsule and *is* virulent. These two forms exist in types that differ in other characters as well. Griffith, in 1927, injected heat-killed cells of S form of Type III along with living R form of Type II under the skin of mice. From the hearts of these mice he later isolated bacteria that turned out to be Type III S! Either there had been an error in the experiment or Type II R had been transformed permanently to Type III S. This kind of one-way recombination between living and dead cells is called *transformation.*

This remarkable experiment was later verified, done with viruses, and done *in vitro* (i.e., in a test tube). Avery and his co-workers simply repeated it *in vitro* and went on to identify the transforming principle. In their words, "A deoxyribonucleic acid fraction has been isolated from Type III pneumococci which is capable of transforming unencapsulated R variants derived from pneumococcus Type II into fully encapsulated Type III cells."

Duplication of Genes

Ultraviolet light, X rays, and various chemicals may cause spontaneous heritable changes in organisms, called mutations. It has been shown that the action spectrum of mutation by ultraviolet light is closely paralleled by the absorption of that light by DNA. In other words, DNA seems to be absorbing most of the energy that causes mutations. It is conceivable that it passes on the energy to some other target that is really the genetic material, but in the light of the identification of the transforming principle as DNA, it is hard to escape the conclusion that DNA is both the ultraviolet absorber and the material of which genes are made.

Deoxyribonucleic acid is an enormous *polymer;* that is, it is put together of repeated units end to end like a chain. The components are deoxyribose, a sugar, phosphate groups, and cyclic compounds containing carbon and nitrogen—collectively purines and pyrimidines. The molecule's precise structure need not concern us here, but we should appreciate its gross structure. The main building block is deoxyribose with attached purine or pyrimidine. These units are linked (polymerized) through phosphate groups to form long chains. The chains, however, are not straight. X-ray diffraction studies by Watson and Crick have shown that the chains are grouped into double-stranded helices (Fig. 5-1). Also, note that there are two purines and two pyrimidines. These groups jut out into the center of the helix and are of such size that a purine may only be opposite a pyrimidine and vice versa. In fact, it is even more precise than that: adenine (purine) aligns only with thymine (pyrimidine), and guanine (purine) aligns only with cytosine; the alignment is fixed by hydrogen bonds. The first remarkable feature of this structure is that in the synthesis of new chains each chain becomes a pattern for the production of its counterpart. This is so because of the relationship of adenime to thymine and guanine to cytosine. If the strands separate and a new strand is synthesized in association with each, the two new daughter double helices will look just like the parent double helix. This is how the Janus-like gene duplicates and maintains its own integrity.

Gene Control of Protein Synthesis

The second notable property lies in the possibility for a large number of sequences of purines and pyrimidines—for instance, ATTGCATCGACCT. This gives a basis for a genetic code. Certain sequences serve as patterns for synthesis of certain RNA "messenger" molecules, which migrate from the chromosomes in the nucleus into the cytoplasm. They carry the message from the genes and produce proteins in cooperation with insoluble RNA particles, the ribosomes —composed of a second kind of RNA—and a third RNA which conveys amino acids to the ribosomes. This is how synthesis of protein is directed by the genes. And this is how the Janus-like gene directs the synthetic metabolism of the cell (see Fig. 5-4, page 51).

The genetic code is discussed again later in this chapter under the heading *Mutation;* another volume in this series—Jensen: *The Plant*

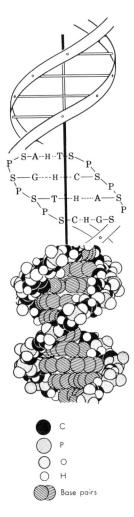

Fig. 5-1. *The helix of DNA, with three different ways of representing the molecular arrangement. Top: general picture of the double helix, with the phosphate-sugar combinations making up the outside spirals and the base pairs the cross-bars; middle: a somewhat more detailed representation: phosphate (P), sugar (S), adenine (A), thymine (T), guanine (G), cytosine (C), and hydrogen (H); bottom: detailed structure showing how the space is filled with atoms: carbon (C), oxygen (O), hydrogen (H), phosphorus (P), and the base pairs. (Reproduced by permission from Carl P. Swanson, The Cell, copyright © 1960 by Prentice-Hall, Inc., Englewood Cliffs, N.J.)*

Cell—presents a thorough-going discussion of protein synthesis. The discovery of how sequences of bases in DNA are ultimately converted to sequences of amino acids in specific proteins is one of the triumphs of mid-twentieth century science. Also read the articles by Crick and Nirenberg, listed in the references at the end of this book, to capture some of the excitement of this discovery.

CONTROL OF GENE ACTION

So far we have gained an idea of what genes are made of and how they carry the message of what kinds of proteins to build. Interest centers on proteins because they make up the enzymes of cells, and enzymes mediate all chemical reactions concerned with metabolism and growth. But this is a static picture. How is gene activity controlled? Does each gene simply produce messenger RNA constantly at the same rate throughout the life of an organism? The organism is growing and differentiating. In the course of differentiation new compounds appear; for example, in differentiation of stem vascular tissues certain cells become lignified. Were proteinaceous enzymes that mediate lignin synthesis pre-existent and subsequently "turned on"? Or were they formed at the appropriate time by "turning on" their governing gene? Answers to these questions are now being sought by students of genetics and development. Just as cytogenetics was born of the marriage of Mendelian genetics and chromosomal cytology, so has developmental genetics been born of the marriage of embryology and genetics, and the marriage has been fertile.

GENE-CONTROL SYSTEMS IN MAIZE

Indian corn, or maize, has been as useful a tool in genetics and cytogenetics as the fruit fly, for an enormous amount of variation exists in its populations, and its inheritance can be analyzed in terms of chromosomal behavior in mitosis and meiosis. Perhaps you have noticed some of its variability: popcorn, sweet corn, field corn, black, white, yellow, red, bronze, and purple kernels, and so forth. These are phenotypic differences that have a genetic basis.

Barbara McClintock, of the Carnegie Institution of Washington at Cold Spring Harbor, New York, has studied corn genetics for years. In the early 1950s she deduced the existence of two classes of genes. The effect of one is expressed "outwardly" in cell cytoplasm and thus phenotypically—as, for instance, in coloration. This class has been termed *structural genes.* The other class, called *controlling genes,* acts entirely within the nucleus by controlling the activities of structural genes. In other words, controlling genes govern the time and rate of action of structural genes. Why has McClintock come to these conclusions?

There is a locus on the third chromosome of maize called the *A locus;* it has been known since the early days of genetics. A_1 is the usual dominant allele; it causes production of red anthocyanin in the diploid plant body and the kernel, which has a diploid embryo and a triploid endosperm (for an explanation of endosperm see Chapter 6, page 69); a_1 is its recessive allele. When a_1 is homozygous, anthocyanin is usually not formed. Now, if red $\dfrac{A_1}{a_1}$ and white $\dfrac{a_1}{a_1}$ plants of race 1 are crossed, most of the kernels formed are red or white. Very rarely, however, a pale red kernel occurs, and pale red is allelic to white and dark red. It was some years after the discovery of the A locus that the rare pale red kernels were first observed. Doubtless this was due to the fact that occurrence of pale red in such a cross is a very uncommon event. If the progenies studied in the early days of corn genetics amounted to a thousand individuals and if an event occurs only once in ten million zygotes, the chance of detecting it would have been only one in ten thousand. Evidently the A locus as a functional unit can be broken up by recombination, but it happens very seldom. In other words, the A locus is a complex locus composed of several tightly linked genes, and crossing-over occurs within it in a vanishingly low frequency. For this reason its complex nature went undetected.

The red, white, and pale red appear as alleles, but, since recombination can occur within them, they are spoken of as *pseudo-alleles.*

The way in which recombination within A_1 and a_1 might give rise to pale red is shown in Table 5-1. Assume that the A_1 red locus is really composed of two tightly linked genes, 1 and 2, together in one chromosome in what is known as the *cis position* with respect to each other. Red kernels will be homozygous for A_1. Assume the a_1 locus to be composed of tightly linked genes 1' and 2' together in one chromosome (in cis position). The white kernels are homozygous for a_1. The heterozygote of these two will be red because of dominance; the 1 and 2 genes in cis position are fully functional. When meiosis takes places in the heterozygote, crossing-over may occur within the locus, giving rise to chromosomes that combine 1 and 2' and 1' and 2. The genes are then said to be in the *trans position.*

Table 5-1. *Hypothetical representation of complex locus A and position effects in maize.*

	Genotype A_1			Phenotype	Genotype A_1			Phenotype
Male chromosome	1	2	cis	Red	1	2	cis	Red
Female chromosome	1	2	cis		1′	2′	cis	
	A_1				a_1			

	a_1			Phenotype	A			Phenotype
Male chromosome	1′	2′	cis	White	1	2′	trans	Pale red
Female chromosome	1′	2′	cis		1′	2	trans	
	a_1				A			
					Crossover types			

This combination of genes is half functional and results in pale red color. The expression of the genes has been influenced by their position relative to each other, which is known as *position effect*. It indicates that some genic interactions depend on the physical juxtaposition of genes in a chromosome.

There is another gene, Dt (called *dotted*), at another locus. A plant homozygous for a_1, which also has Dt in its genome, has streaks of anthocyanin in its leaves and a white kernel with red dots. Dt is assumed to have caused a_1 to mutate to alleles, such as A_1, that produce color. The size of the dot or the length of the stripe indicate how early in development the mutation took place. The number of dots and stripes indicates the frequency of mutation. When Dt is absent, a_1 is quite stable. The Dt gene has been found in different chromosomes in different races and is subject to frequent transposition within the genome. By planned breeding it is possible to get diploid plants with, say, from one to four Dt genes. When this is done, the mutation rate is found to be directly proportional to the dosage of Dt.

When the pale red type of race I was crossed with Dt-carrying plants, the kernels produced were dotted dark red on a pale red background. That is, Dt acted in the same way as before in creating dots, but *the shades produced were different,* because it was acting on different A-locus gene complexes.

When red homozygous A_1 individuals of another race were self-pollinated, a low frequency of pale red mutants arose by crossover within the compound locus, as in race I. When this new stock was bred with a Dt-containing plant, *no* dots were formed. Evidently a gene that responded to the Dt gene was present in race I. In the second pale red race it was lacking, and therefore no dots were formed. This responding gene has been called an *operator*. Thus, there appear to be two controlling elements: the *regulator* (Dt in this case), which can be any place in the genome and can be transposed even within the life of the organism; and the *operator,* which is activated by the regulator. The operator is probably situated next to the structural gene in a compound locus (see Fig. 5-4, page 51).

GENE-CONTROL SYSTEMS IN BACTERIA

Existence of a specific regulatory system within the nucleus was known only in maize until 1959. In that year a similar system was found in bacteria. One has also been identified in bacteriophage viruses, and it now appears likely that they will be found in all organisms.

Induced Enzyme Synthesis

Discovery of a three-component system in bacteria is a recent event, but its impetus goes back to the turn of this century when certain enzymes of micro-organisms were found to be produced only in the presence of the specific substrate on which they acted. For example, *Escherichia coli,* which is a bacterium living in the colon of humans, can be grown under artificial conditions in which it is provided with needed nutrients, salts, and vitamins and necessary moisture and temperature conditions. When *E. coli* is grown with maltose as its carbon and energy source, it is able to ferment it. If lactose is then substituted for maltose, the bacterium will not immediately ferment lactose, but will be able to do so after a lag period. Enzymes for fermenting lactose were not present in appreciable amounts before lactose was present. Lactose *induced* production of the very enzymes that are capable of breaking it down. This is called *enzyme induction.* The actual increase of enzyme is about 1,000- to 10,000-fold.

What happens if two carbon sources are present at the same time? Will enzymes that break them down be equally abundant? Probably not, for one may be suppressed. This is shown when *E. coli* is grown on a mixture of glucose and lactose; glucose is metabolized first. There is a lag and then the lactose is fermented. Glucose suppresses formation of the enzyme beta-galactosidase, which is needed for lactose fermentation. The suppression is brought about by a small molecule nutrient or *metabolite* (an intermediate product of metabolism) called the *repressor*. It may be some product near the end of a chain of metabolic steps, acting back on synthesis of enzymes involved in early steps of the sequence. In Fig. 5-2, nutrient A induces synthesis

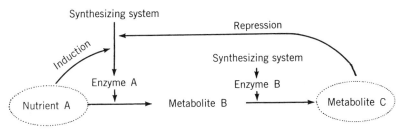

Fig. 5-2. *Schematic representation of induction and repression of enzymes in a metabolic pathway.*

of enzyme A, which results in the nutrient's transformation to substance B. Enzyme B converts it to metabolite C, but metabolite C acts back repressingly on synthesis of enzyme A. This reaction is called *feedback repression.* Necessary production of enzymes is thus promoted by the presence of the chemical on which they act, and needless overproduction is prevented by some useful product as it reaches optimal levels.

Induction and repression are interrelated phenomena, for inducers and repressors act antagonistically in controlling production of enzymes.

Constitutive enzymes are either present or absent; they are not subject to the kind of control described above.

The Lactose-Fermenting System

Let's look more closely at the lactose-fermenting system in *E. coli* to get a better understanding of these concepts. Lactose can only induce beta-galactosidase formation when it gets inside the cell. The cell membrane governs passage of some molecules, while others cross it in accordance with the laws of diffusion. Lactose is a "governed" molecule. It is taken up by an energy-requiring process and can be concentrated against a diffusion gradient and maintained at concentrations much higher than those that prevail in the external milieu. This property lies at the basis of life; it allows cells to preserve their organization in spite of random processes tending to create disorder. Now it so happens that in the cell membrane an enzyme has been found that mediates the passage of lactose from the extra- to the intra-cellular space. This carrier molecule has been called galactoside permease. Both it and beta-galactosidase are inducible by galactosides. Indeed, they are both induced by the same inducer. That they are discrete is shown by the fact that mutants exist which can accumulate galactosides but cannot ferment them. Mutants that cannot produce permease still retain the capacity to form galactosidase. This system is diagrammed in Fig. 5-3.

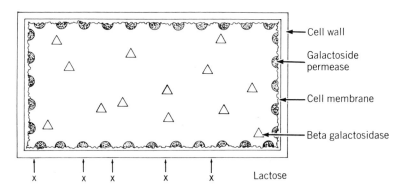

Fig. 5-3. *Location of the enzymes galactoside permease and beta galactosidase in the bacterial cell.*

The lactose-fermenting system can be interpreted in terms of genes controlling enzyme synthesis by assuming the existence of a regulatory gene, located anywhere in the genome, that produces a substance inhibitory to operator genes associated with the structural genes (see Fig. 5-4). In the absence of a small molecule inducer (such as nutrient A in Fig. 5-2), the regulator gene inhibits the operator, causing inactivity of the structural gene. The small molecule inducer acts by nullifying the effect of the regulator gene. A repressor substance (metabolite C in Fig. 5-2) may compete with the inducer by preoccupying some site on the inhibitory substance produced by the regulator gene, thus preserving the inhibitory effect.

If the regulatory gene is inactivated by some chemical change (mutation), then repression of operators should be impossible and the

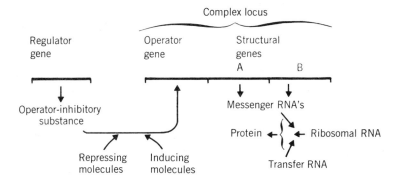

Fig. 5-4. *Regulator-operator model for control of gene action.*

structural genes should be constantly active. In other words, the enzyme is always produced and therefore appears constitutive. Also, the effect of inactivation of the regulator may be *pleiotropic* (affecting more than one character), because the regulator may have command over more than one operator and each operator may govern more than one structural gene. We have seen this to be the case in *E. coli* where permease and galactosidase are under common control. Both become constitutive enzymes when their common regulator gene mutates.

If this model for control is correct, then mutations of the operator, which abolish its repressibility but not its activity in causing structural genes to produce messenger RNA, should also give rise to constitutive synthesis of enzyme. Constitutiveness should thus be dominant to repressibility, and the mutation should be pleiotropic. This in fact happens. Mutants of *E. coli* that constitutively produce galactosidase and permease have been isolated. The mutant is dominant, and, when mapped by recombination, it is found to be located in the *Lac* region, where the structural genes lie. Hence it is not allelic with the regulator gene, i, which is located elsewhere in the genome.

CYCLIC ACTIVITY OF GENES

McClintock has found that activity of a certain regulator gene in maize, Spm, may be turned on and off in the course of development of a given plant, or its cycle may be much slower, so that it remains in the active or inactive state through generations before reverting to the other state. Similar cyclic activity has been found by Lederberg and Iino in the flagellated bacterium, *Salmonella*. As one structural gene, H_2, becomes active, another, H_1, becomes inactive. H_1 can only be active when H_2 is turned off. The significance and mechanism of these recent startling discoveries are not yet known and are subjects of current research. They seem to indicate another case where complex and simple organisms have common properties. Perhaps they, too, will have a common explanation.

The controlling-element (regulator, operator), structural-gene hypothesis is one of the most fruitful ideas in modern genetics. It explains regulatory systems in organisms as diverse as maize, bacteria, and virus. Furthermore, it can explain pseudo-allelism, position effects, and certain cases of pleiotropy. As geneticists and biochemists have developed finer methods of analysis, they have succeeded in formulating ever more powerful generalizations. The wonder is that the basic Mendelian ideas remain valid, a crude but solid framework that newer thoughts strengthen and give detail. Recent advances in knowledge have entailed greater complexity as well as understanding.

MUTATION

We have spoken of mutation several times already, because the concept was needed in earlier discussions. But now let's look closer at it.

Hugo de Vries, a great Dutch biologist, formulated the mutation theory just a few years after the rediscovery of Mendel's paper. He defined mutation as a spontaneous heritable change. He discovered it while studying the genetics of an evening primrose, *Oenothera lamarkiana*. One offspring was much larger than its parent. Subsequent investigation showed that it was a polyploid with 28 chromosomes (tetraploid). Other deviant individuals were later found to have duplications for entire chromosomes. Thus they had 15 instead of the normal 14 chromosomes. Although these were not changes at the gene level, they were spontaneous heritable changes.

Specific sequences-of-three of the purine and pyrimidine nitrogenous bases in DNA form "words," which ultimately cause specific amino acids to be incorporated into proteins. If the "spelling" of a single "word" is altered by exchanging one of its bases for another, the resulting base sequence may not make sense, because no amino acid corresponds to this sequence. An amino acid may thus be left out of the protein in the formation of which this "word" takes part. The protein is altered; a mutation has occurred. This is a *nonsense* sort of mutation. On the other hand, the new sequence of three bases ("word") may make sense but be the code word for a quite different amino acid. In this event, a different amino acid is inserted at that position in the protein. The protein is changed; a mutation has occurred. This is a *mis-sense* mutation.

Both types of mutations are *intra-genic,* caused by chemical changes in DNA. They are thus mutations at the molecular level. They have been called *point* mutations to distinguish them from mutations due to chromosomal alterations or position effects.

In view of the many ways in which mutation can occur, it is remarkable how rare an event it is in nature. On the average, a single gene will mutate in only one in a million cells in a given generation. Looked at another way, if *Drosophila* has from five to ten thousand genes, one gamete out of 20 has a new mutation.

Mutation is caused by natural and man-made ionizing radiation and chemicals such as mustard gas and nitrous oxide. High temperature increases mutation rate, and even genes that cause other genes in the same genome to mutate are known in some organisms. The mechanisms whereby these agents cause mutation are being actively studied, for man is well aware that he is increasing the level of radiation and chemical mutagens in his environment. An understanding of the mechanisms may help in finding ways of reducing mutation; and, furthermore, the study of mutation is intimately associated with the study of cancer.

Mutations can occur in the somatic cells of the organism; for example, in corn they give rise to unique cells and cell lineages in the form of dots or stripes. In multicellular plants these mutant cells may later become the progenitors of the germ cells. In multicellular animals, on the other hand, somatic mutations won't be transmitted to offspring because gamete-producing cells are set aside in the gonads early in development. Mutations immediately affect survival of unicellular organisms, and are immediately reproduced if they do not impair the cell's fitness.

The most important thing about mutation is that it is the sole source of new genetic building blocks. Another important feature is that it is at random with regard to the adaptive effects of the particular change. Recombination can occur by any of the means described earlier and will permit all possible combinations of genes to be made, but only mutation can provide new structural genes, which create new molecular configurations in enzymes and their products.

Since mutation is a rather rare event, it is not surprising that, in the ebb and flow of populations, recombination has been so richly exploited.

6

FROM GENE

TO CHARACTER:

THE MODE OF

GENE ACTION

The descriptive aspects of plant development are covered elsewhere in this series, so this chapter attempts only to present some principles and to establish a way of looking at development as the spinning out of a tapestry whose plan is laid down in the message of the genetic material.

PHENOTYPE AND GENOTYPE

Johannsen, a Danish biologist working in the first decade of this century, took a bean plant and inbred it for a number of generations to produce a homozygous population. This is called a *pure line,* because all individuals have the same genetic constitution. He grew such plants under as uniform conditions as possible, and then gathered their seeds and weighed them. He found an average weight, but all the seeds were not exactly alike in size. They varied around a mean value (Fig. 6-1). He then took large seeds and grew plants from them, and also did the same thing with small seeds. The mean value for seed weight proved to be the same for these two groups of plants. What is more, this mean value was equal that of the parental value. This result showed that even where the genotype is similar, development may differ, giving rise to different phenotypes. In other words, a certain lability is possible in development.

This experiment also demonstrated an important rule in plant or animal breeding: selection for a certain characteristic—increased size, for instance—will be effective only when there is genetic variability in control of the characteristic in the population on which se-

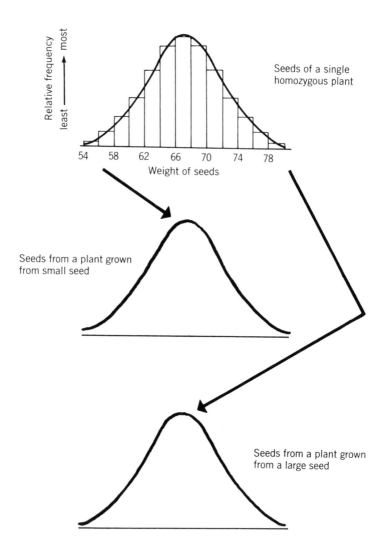

Fig. 6-1. *Johannsen's classical experiment on beans.*

lection is being practiced. Choosing large bean seeds as progenitors does not increase average seed size, because their genotypes are the same as those of small seeds.

About the same time, Tschermak was raising winter and summer races of rye; summer type was found to be dominant to winter. But the ratio obtained from a cross depended on the time of year the seeds were planted. Raising them in summer yielded more summer (annual) types, and in winter more winter types. This led him to a greater appreciation of the fact it is not the character but the potentiality to develop it that is inherited. This potentiality is the genotype or genetic message encoded in DNA; its expression is subject to external influences. Of course, this is implicit in the fact that development often begins with a single cell that is quite characterless. With cell multiplication and diversification, complexity and characters are developed. Nevertheless, we sometimes forget that it is the potentiality *for* development, not the final product *of* it, that is inherited.

DEVELOPMENT

Development is a process of regulated growth and differentiation which occurs as a result of interaction of genome with cytoplasm, internal cellular environment, and external environment (see Fig. 6-2). Interaction between cytoplasm and nucleus is well illustrated by

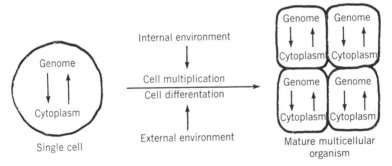

Fig. 6-2. *Interactions producing development.*

feedback repression, described in the last chapter; but what is meant by internal cellular and external environments?

A virus consists of a complex of several enormous molecules of RNA or DNA and protein. It can be crystallized like any other molecule. Its development consists of the reproduction of this complex by the host cell that the virus has infected, and is essentially a chemical reaction (Fig. 6-3) involving polymerizing and orienting molecules. Development results from interaction of virus particle, host cell nucleus, and cytoplasm. Effects of external environment are felt only indirectly through the host cell's internal milieu.

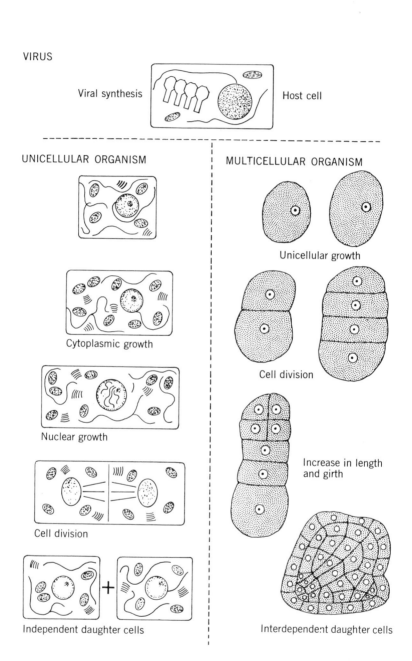

Fig. 6-3. *Development at different levels of existence.*

Development of unicellular organisms involves increase of cell mass and subsequent division to produce two daughter cells similarly constituted. Here there is an exceedingly complex system of different molecules whose physiological function depends on their assuming precisely ordered forms: membranes, plastids, chromosomes, etc. Development takes place inside a parent cell, usually in an aquatic medium. The cells do not cause differences to arise among themselves through mutual influences. Differentiation is at a subcellular level. Where differences do occur between genetically identical cells, they are due to differences in the external environment. We have seen, for example, how different enzymes may be induced by different sugars. Another instance is provided by some unicellular algae, where pigment development depends on the wavelength of light impinging on the cell.

The genome of the multicullular organism interacts with the cytoplasm in the zygote to bring about growth and cell division. The cells remain together. Further divisions cause the cell mass to increase in size. No longer is each cell exposed to similar environmental conditions, for a new internal environment has been created. This is the aforementioned internal cellular environment. Cells to the center— or more generally speaking, differently positioned in the mass—are subjected to different conditions. Gradients in concentration of minerals, gases, and metabolites become established. Also, the internal cellular milieu will be subject to less fluctuation, because the outermost cells form a protective barrier, keeping water, salts, metabolites, etc., either in or out. It will differ from the external environment to the extent that the anatomy, morphology, and physiology of the organism, working together, are able to regulate it. The cells are subjected to differences along many gradients. Induction and repression may come into play, turning on and off enzyme synthesis; genes may act cyclically as in *Salmonella* or maize; transposition of regulators and operators may take place. These processes might go on serially or in combination to bring about the differentiation characteristic of the adult organism.

This view of differentiation is very speculative, but worth presenting because it indicates the complexity of development and some of the avenues of investigation. Perhaps no question in biology is farther from being answered than that of how development is regulated.

Production of a new enzyme in a cell can cause a chain reaction, for it can produce a new substance that reacts back on the genome

to cause production of yet another substance. In this way difference
may be built on difference and divergence of cells proceed. This concept is called epigenesis: succeeding events in differentiation are built
on earlier ones. It can be illustrated with some examples.

Normally, sporangia in ferns are borne on the under side of sporophytic leaves (Fig. 6-4); however, if gametophytes are subjected to
appropriate conditions, sporangia are borne directly on them. An

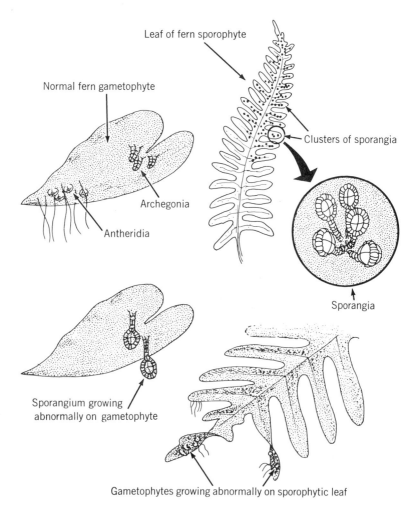

Fig. 6-4. *Abnormal occurrence of gametangia and
sporangia in ferns.*

event occurs in a single cell which leads the derivatives of that cell down a developmental pathway normally found in the other phase of the life cycle. Similarly, gametophytes normally develop from germinating haploid spores. When leaves are placed flat on moist soil, however, diploid gametophytes are produced on them. Here again, differentiation proceeds to an endpoint along a particular pathway. Certain differentiative steps set the stage for others that follow.

A beautiful example of epigenesis has been worked out recently in *Sordaria macrospora,* an ascomycetous fungus closely related to *Neurospora.* It is bisexual and self-fertile. The sequence of sexual development begins with formation of the female gametangium (*ascogonium*) and is followed by fusion of cells (*plasmogamy*) without fusion of nuclei. This leads to development of *meiosporangia* (called *asci*), fusion of nuclei (*karyogamy*), meiosis, spore maturation, and maturation of the fruiting body that holds them. Esser and Straub, German geneticists, irradiated a wild, *self-fertile* strain with X rays and obtained 18 mutant strains that were *self-sterile* when grown alone. Of these 18, some produced only vegetative mycelia; some, female gametangia but no fruiting body; some, sterile fruiting bodies; and others, fertile fruiting bodies but nondischarging asci. Each of these types was produced more than once by mutation, and when crosses were made between individuals of the same mutant class, no more advanced stage of development occurred. But when crosses were made between members of different classes, normal fruiting bodies were formed—i.e., normal spores were released. This indicated that each mutant type, through the mutation of a single gene, lost its ability to form a specific factor for normal differentiation, and each stage was dependent on the immediately preceding stage. When nuclei of two different classes were brought together, they complemented one another, each making up for the deficiency in the other nucleus. Normal development resulted. Fourteen loci were involved in the epigenetic sequence of sexual differentiation. No doubt more loci will be found to be implicated in this complex chain of events. The bisexual, self-fertile organism has within it genes making possible development through the complete sequence of stages. These stages can be diagrammed as follows:

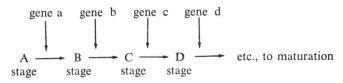

Unisexual types, however, which reproduce only in association with a member of the opposite sex, evidently have only partial sequences that must be complemented by those of the mating partner. John Raper, an American biologist, has proven this by ingenious experiments with the water mold *Achlya* (Phycomycetes).

Vegetative hyphae of male and female plants are indistinguishable, but when they grow together a sequence of changes occurs in the following order: (1) randomly oriented antheridial hyphae arise on the male plant; (2) oogonial initials arise on the female hyphae; (3) antheridial hyphae grow directly toward the ripened oogonial initial; (4) on reaching the oogonium, each antheridial hypha becomes appressed to it and branches into a "hand-like" structure; (5) a wall forms at the wrist of the hand so that a multinucleate antheridium is formed; (6) a wall forms between the globose oogonial initial and its stalk, cutting off a multinucleate oogonium; (7) each nucleus in the oogonium becomes the center of organization of an egg; (8) small tubes grow from antheridium into the oogonium where they contact the eggs; (9) each egg receives an antheridial nucleus, and karyogamy soon follows; (10) each zygote is invested by a thick wall and enters a dormant period.

A slowly flowing stream of water was passed successively over a number of plants in Lilliputian aquaria. This process established the order and origin of the principal hormones. For example, when the water passed from male 1 to female 1 to male 2 to female 2, nothing visible happened to the first male and female, but the second male produced antheridial hyphae, and the second female, oogonial initials. When the water was passed from female 1 to male 1 to female 2 to male 2 nothing appeared to happen to female 1; antheridial hyphae were produced in both males; oogonial initials were formed in the second female; and in the farthest downstream male, antheridial hyphae grew directly toward the point where water entered its tank from tank 3. Thus, the whole process is started by some substance(s) from the female which triggers off antheridial formation in the male; the latter in turn produces a substance that causes initiation of oogonial initials. When this occurs, the female secretes a chemotrophic hormone, causing antheridia to grow toward oogonia. When the male and female are grown in the same dish, but separated by a membrane, it can be shown that the fourth to seventh steps, as outlined above, are also under hormonal control. Thus at least seven distinct hormones are involved in this sexual developmental sequence, and the genes responsible for the production of these hormones are partitioned between the male and female. We can diagram the probable interaction between them as follows:

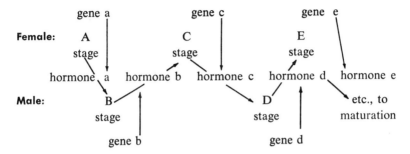

We see here how sexual dimorphism results from partitioning (between male and female) the genes mediating epigenesis of sex organs and cells. Sometimes both complete sequences for differentiation of male and female parts exist in the same genome, which indicates a completely bisexual organism. This type grades into those that are fully male and partially female or fully female and partially male, and eventually to those that are fully unisexual, like *Achlya,* which is haploid. The male has the antheridial sequence, and the female has the oogonial sequence. Genes that coordinate development of the two exist as well. The ascomycete, *Sordaria,* is bisexual and haploid; gene sequences for male and female organs are incorporated into the haploid genome.

A final example that supports this idea of partitioning of sequences comes from an experiment by Elie and Emil Marchal, Belgians working in the first decade of this century. Some mosses are unisexual (*dioecious*) in that a gametophyte bears either antheridium or archegonium. In the Marchals' experiment, no matter how external conditions were varied or whether new plants were regenerated from them, a haploid gametophyte always retained its given sex. It was already known that male and female genomes are joined in the zygote, from which a sporophyte develops, and that sex factors segregate at meiosis, giving two male meiospores to each two female ones. The Marchals cut small pieces of the sporophyte stalk and, by placing them in the proper conditions, were able to get them to regenerate into diploid gametophytes. When such gametophytes matured they formed both antheridia and archegonia; they were bisexual! The developmental sequences had been brought together in one genome.

LABILITY IN DEVELOPMENT: CHANGE IN FORM

As a bacterial cell is capable of forming different enzymes in response to different inducing substances and thereby gaining biochemical flexibility, so can a higher plant take on different forms in response to differences in the environment. Flexibility in form, like biochemical flexibility, gives the organism a chance to withstand fluctuations in the external environment. The aquatic buttercup is one of many aquatic or amphibious plants with this property (Fig. 6-5). A much-divided leaf is formed under water, while on the

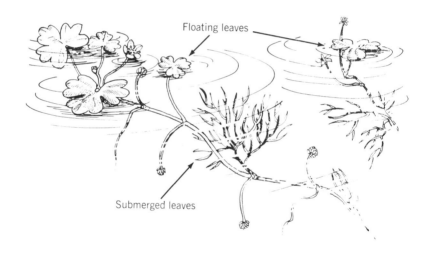

Floating leaves

Submerged leaves

Fig. 6-5. *Developmental flexibility of the water buttercup.* (*From H. L. Mason,* A Flora of the Marshes of California. *Berkeley: University of California Press, 1957.*)

surface a flat, undivided leaf is produced. The genotype of the organism remains constant, but the phenotype changes in harmony with changes in the environment.

LABILITY IN DEVELOPMENT: CHANGE OF SEX

Sometimes the sexual functioning of the organism changes in response to environmental stimuli. Jellyfish belong to a primitive class of animals, Coelenterates, one of which, *Bougainvillia* (not to be confused with the colorful tropical vine *Bougainvillea*), will illustrate how, under different conditions, an organism can change sex even though its genotype remains constant.

An embryo comes to rest on a rock and grows into a tubular structure—a *stolon*—which grows in length by cell division near the tip. The apical region develops into a sac-like structure—the *hydranth*—which has tentacles and which is capable of catching food. The basal portion of the stolon branches repeatedly to form a root-like attachment to the rock. Subsequent growth in length goes on in the region just below the apical hydranth, and it is here, too, that budding out of secondary branches occurs. A complex organism is formed by this budding and growth in length. High or rising temperatures favor rapid linear growth and, therefore, stolons. Low or falling temperatures favor slow, radial growth and, therefore, hydranths. Still lower temperatures trigger medusa development (Fig. 6-6). Medusae are like jellyfish; they become detached from the parental system, bear eggs and sperm, and thus represent the sexual phase of development. The hydranth and stolons represent the vegetative phase. There exists considerable plasticity in the over-all form of *Bougainvillia,* and it is brought about by growth-rate differences at different temperatures.

Whether the medusa bears eggs, sperm, or both depends on growth rate, too: where rapid growth prevails, eggs are formed; where medium, eggs and sperm; and where slow, only sperm. Growth rates here may be influenced by temperature or food supply. So the actual sex as well as the change from vegetative to reproductive phase is influenced by the environment.

The acorn squash, *Cucurbita pepo,* is a vine that produces a single flower in each leaf axil. The first fertile flowers to develop are *staminate* (have only stamens); they are followed by flowers that have carpels and no stamens. Plants like this, which bear both staminate and ovulate flowers, are called *monoecious.* If the plant experiences high temperatures and long days, staminate flowers continue to be produced. Low temperatures and short days have the opposite effect—they hasten development of ovulate flowers. Similar effects have been described in other monoecious species and in some *dioecious* ones that bear either staminate or ovulate flowers (but not both). Even in plants in which a single flower has both stamens and carpels (hermaphroditic flowers), the environmental conditions that favor carpels may not be those favoring optimal growth of stamens.

Environmental conditions apparently act through altering auxin

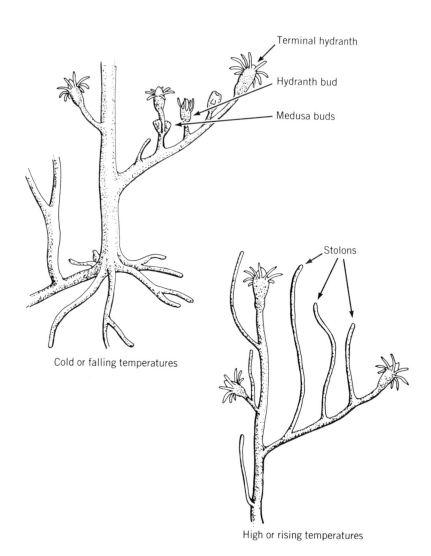

Terminal hydranth

Hydranth bud

Medusa buds

Stolons

Cold or falling temperatures

High or rising temperatures

Fig. 6-6. *Effect of temperature on development of the coelenterate animal* Bougainvillia. (*From* Growth, Development, and Pattern *by N. J. Berrill. San Francisco: W. H. Freeman and Company, 1961.*)

levels within the plants. High auxin levels promote femaleness and low levels promote maleness. Although the mechanism of these reactions is not understood, we see here another illustration of how the phenotypic expression of a genotype can be affected by environment and, specifically, how there may be lability in development of sexual characteristics.

LABILITY IN DEVELOPMENT: LIFE CYCLES IN PLANTS

Change from vegetative to reproductive phase in *Bougainvillia* occurs all within the diploid tissues of the animal—development is simply shunted down different pathways by a triggering mechanism. All cells of multicellular animals are diploid, with the exception of their gametes, which are haploid. Theirs is called a *diplontic life cycle* (Fig. 6-7). All higher plants and many algae and fungi have another sort of life cycle—*haplo-diplontic*. It is given this name because a haploid phase exists between meiosis and fertilization (Fig. 6-8). The products of meiosis are not eggs and sperms but meiospores, which, instead of fusing to form a diploid zygote, undergo mitotic divisions and develop into haploid individuals. These then eventually bear the gametes; hence they are called *gametophytes*. The diploid individual growing from the zygote is the site of meiosis, and because it forms the meiospores it is called the sporophyte. Ferns offer a good example of such a life cycle (Fig. 6-9). In this case the change of form is under rather strong genetic control, triggered by some reaction related to meiosis, fertilization, or differences in environments in which meiospore and zygote develop. But we have already seen that sporangia can be induced to form on gametophytes and gametophytes on the leaves of sporophytes without meiosis; so change of form is not controlled by chromosome number itself.

The gymnosperms—cycads, *Ginkgo,* and conifers, for example— have the same basic haplo-diplontic alternation of generation as the fern (Fig. 6-10). However, two kinds of meiospore are produced in them: one that develops into a *microgametophyte* (*micro* = little), which bears sperms, and another that develops into a *megagametophyte* (*mega* = big), which bears an egg. Furthermore, these gametophytes differ from those of ferns in developing right inside the meiospore cell membrane and usually also in being nonphotosynthetic. The egg is borne in an archegonium that is much simpler than the fern's. Most significantly, the megagametophyte and megaspore are retained inside the megasporangium, and thus inside the parental

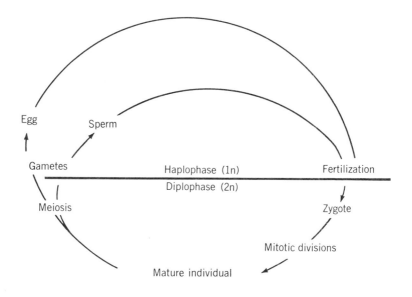

Fig. 6-7. *Diplontic life cycle as found in higher animals and some algae.*

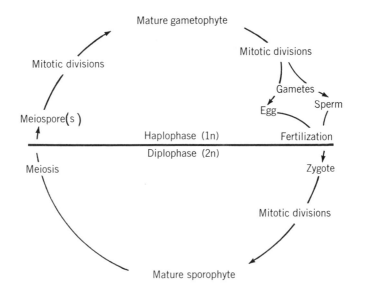

Fig. 6-8. *Haplo-diplontic life cycle in plants.*

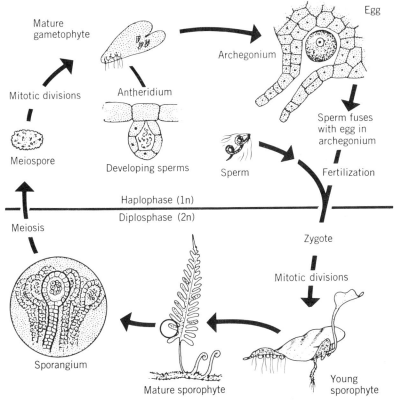

Fig. 6-9. *Alternation of phase in ferns (haplo-diplontic plants).*

sporophyte tissues. There they are protected and, with the latter tissues, eventually form a seed. The gametophytic generations are unisexual and no longer free-living organisms.

In angiosperms, the trend of reduction of gametophyte has gone even further: fewer mitotic divisions occur in the microspore, so that mature microgametophytes have only three nuclei; also, instead of three megaspores dying, the four megaspores resulting from meiosis of a megasporocyte may all survive. They remain within the megasporocyte membrane and all experience one mitotic division. In this way they form a mature megagametophyte having eight nuclei. One nucleus is the egg; two others associate and fuse with a sperm to produce the *primary endosperm nucleus.* This triploid nucleus divides mitotically to form *endosperm,* a tissue specialized for nourishing

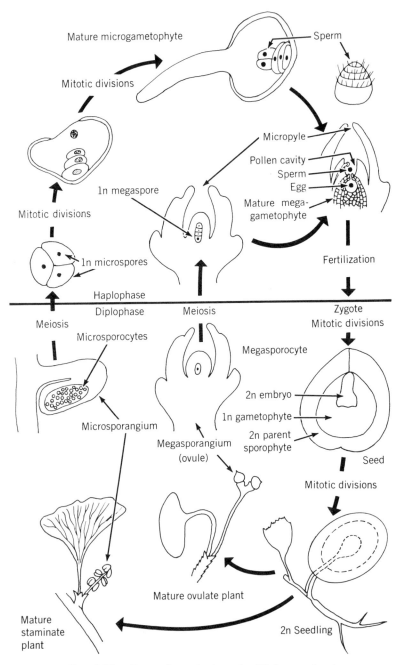

Fig. 6-10. *Alternation of phase in Ginkgo, a haplodiplontic gymnosperm.*

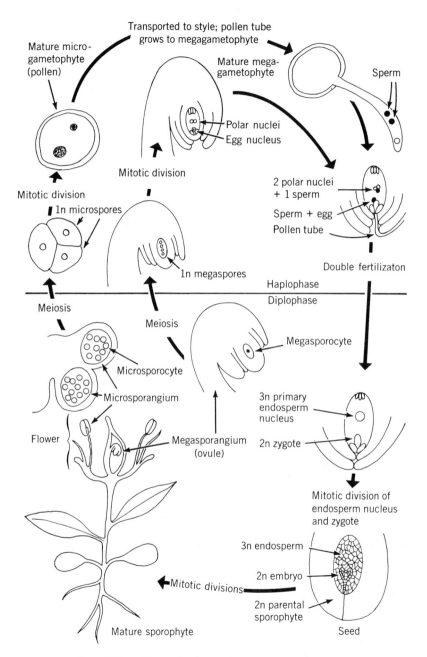

Fig. 6-11. *Alternation of phase in an angiosperm (haplo-diplontic with polyploid endosperm).*

the developing embryo. The remaining nuclei of the gametophyte play an ancillary role. There are numerous variations of this scheme, but most often the female gametophyte is reduced to eight nuclei—much smaller than in gymnosperms—and there is an entirely new tissue created by fusion of a second sperm nucleus with two (sometimes one, sometimes more than two) gametophyte nuclei. Finally, as the life-cycle diagram indicates, the ovule is enclosed within maternal sporophytic tissues. There seems to have been a tendency in evolution to produce an egg within an egg within an egg arrangement: the embryo develops within a gametophyte that is within a megasporangium (ovule) that is within a leaf-like carpel.

Looking back, lability in development, whether it be change of form of one individual, change from asexual to sexual phase of individuals in a diplontic life cycle, or change from haploid to diploid phase in a haplo-diplontic life cycle, is nothing but a special case of differentiation in the widest sense. Even sexuality is a special case of differentiation.

SEXUAL DIFFERENTIATION

One *Bougainvillia* medusa may bear both eggs and sperms. Thus, in the species there is differentiation in gametes but not in the gamete-bearing individual. The same may be said for the fern: one gametophyte produces both eggs and sperms, and only one kind of gametophyte exists.

In most higher animals (man included), however, the individual bearing eggs is distinct from that bearing sperm. The situation is somewhat different and more complex in higher plants; there are two kinds of meiospore: one produces the gametophyte that bears sperm (the pollen), and the other produces a gametophyte that bears the egg. Both kinds of spore are usually formed on one sporophyte (bisporic plants), often in the stamens and ovules of one flower. The maidenhair tree (*Ginkgo biloba*) illustrates those higher plants in which each kind of spore is found on only one individual (unisporic or dioecious plants). In holly and date palms, too, pollen- and seed-bearing plants are distinct.

Sexuality in its most primitive form consisted of an exchange of genetic material between two morphologically though not necessarily genetically identical cells. Subsequent evolution has involved differentiation into egg and sperm at the haploid level and change from bisexuality (cf. *Bougainvillia* and fern) to unisexuality (higher animals) or unisporicness (higher plants) at the diploid level. It has also affected ability to self-fertilize, but this will be discussed in Chapter 9. Thus, sexual differentiation has proceeded from within to between individuals. Differentiation within individuals may be caused by turning on and off certain genes so that developmental pathways are followed either to eggs or sperms. In *Bougainvillia* temperature and nutrition acted as the environmental triggers that ultimately determined the pathways. But to have a clear separation of ability to produce one or the other sex cell, the genes controlling their respective developments must be relegated to separate individuals; there must be a clear-cut difference in genome.

One kind of system could meet this requirement: where one sex differs from the other by a single factor or single group of factors. Fig. 6-12 shows one parent homozygous for "sex factor" and the other heterozygous. When they mate, homozygotes and heterozygotes will appear in a ratio of one to one. This is in fact what happens when there is a 1 : 1 sex ratio in the population (where males equal females). In the most advanced cases (*Ginkgo,* insects, or mammals, for example), the difference goes beyond the genic and can be seen as a difference in morphology of the chromosomes bearing the sex factors. Indeed, the discovery of difference in chromosome morphology between females and males was one of the most conclusive bits of evidence in favor of the chromosomal theory of inheritance. E. B.

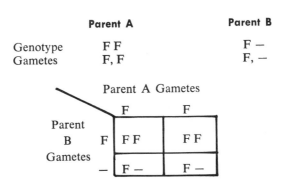

Fig. 6-12. *Hypothetical scheme to account for sexual dualism. (F stands for sex factor.)*

Wilson makes the interesting observation in his monumental book *The Cell in Development and Heredity* (p. 743) that "Mendel himself suggested the possibility that sex-determination might be a phenomenon of heredity and segregation." And he notes further that it was Correns in 1907 who provided definite evidence for this.

Whether the female or the male is homozygous for the sex chromosome (i.e., homogametic) depends on the plant or animal: *females* of *Ginkgo,* many insects, mammals, and reptiles are homogametic. Butterfly and bird *males* are homogametic.

7

REPRODUCTION

AND FITNESS

Chapters 2 to 6 examined the ways in which inheritance is achieved. Chapters 7 to 10 are concerned with fitting genetics into the more general problem of reproduction and adaptation, and in showing how sexuality is of central significance in adapting the organism and its progeny to existence in an ever changing world.

REPRODUCTION

Reproduction is so basic to life that it is even one of life's defining properties. But why is it necessary? The obvious answer is that living things die. Why? This is a question man has long puzzled over. It has many answers.

Organisms die through accident. They are exceedingly intricate machines and are easily destroyed by mechanical injury, poisoning, disease, predation, desiccation, starvation, fire—countless chance events. Naturally and unnaturally occurring ionizing radiation may inactivate genes and upset balanced cell functioning. Everything has a probability of being exposed to it. In short, there is a basic probability of death to which everything is exposed. Species differ in this probability because of inherent physiological and morphological properties. In general, the larger and more complex are able to preserve their internal environments within tolerable limits in spite of wide fluctuations in external conditions. They are thus able to remain active and survive longer under a greater range of conditions than smaller, simpler organisms. We can picture this risk of death as a half-life, analogous to half-lives of the radioactive isotopes. Half the population will decay within a specific span of time.

Longevity

Organisms also die because they have an inherent normal life span or longevity whose physiological basis is very poorly understood.

Man may live from 70 to 80 years; horses, 20; a queen bee, 7; a fruit fly, 50 days; some annual plants, a few months; some trees, a few thousand years. There is an immense range. However, there does seem to be a rough correlation between ability to form new cells and length of life. Most long-lived organisms such as trees or tortoises continue to grow throughout life.

The average life expectancy of a seed crop, a batch of fertilized eggs, or a litter is a function of both death from accident and death from inherent causes. In some species—most plants, for instance— infant mortality is very high, and huge numbers of offspring are produced, while only a few hardy and lucky individuals survive to the old-age characteristic of the group. Birds have a lower infant mortality but a high death rate, with the result that seldom does an individual live out the physiologically possible life span. Modern, technologically advanced man has a low infant mortality, and many of his numbers live out the normal life span and die at more or less the same age.

Even though we are unable to say much regarding the physiological basis for an inherent normal life span, we can gain deeper understanding of reproduction by asking why there should have evolved on earth organisms with such diverse inherent life spans.

Before proceeding, however, it will be helpful to discuss some of the concepts introduced by Charles Darwin and Alfred Russell Wallace in the mid-nineteenth century. Both men were remarkable observers of natural phenomena and independently pondered the question of why there is such a diversity of living things on earth. It had been suggested, long before, that the diversity came about by evolution—that is, by change of one species into another in the course of time. But what causes evolution? They found the answer in the relative viability and reproductive success of organisms under various environmental conditions. Assume a population of plants the members of which can interbreed; they are adapted to their environment—that is to say, they are adjusted to it, and can exist and reproduce in it. If the environment changes—becomes drier, for example—they may not be able to set as much seed; their numbers may dwindle. If, however, a mutation should occur (or have been latent) in some members of the population, which renders them better adjusted to the new conditions, they will reproduce more offspring than the original forms. They have *adapted* to the new conditions by genetic change; they are said to be more *fit,* because their genotypes will predominate in time. Finally, the population, its makeup somewhat modified, will perhaps rise again to its former level. By a natural process, certain forms have died off and others have replaced them. This process is called *natural selection*, and it resulted, in our example above, in *adaptive genetic change* or *evolution*. The mutation-induced change in individual development, which caused the new genotype to be selected, is said to be of *selective advantage*.

Adaptation refers to the *manner* by which an organism succeeds in surviving. For instance, some plants survive drought by being dormant as seeds, others by having lost their leaves, and others by having leathery leaves that retain water. They are adapted in different ways to a particular climate. They may not be equally *fit*, however, when grown together under similar conditions—one or another may reproduce more effectively and so compete the others out of existence. *Fitness* is a measure of the effectiveness of reproduction—that is, the contribution to ensuing generations.

Longevity is intimately related to adaptation, not so much of the individual as of the population of which it is a member. This can be seen from a consideration of the correlations of longevity with other biological attributes. Small organisms usually reach sexual maturity faster than large ones; or, put another way, small organisms have a shorter average time from one generation to the next. Also, they have short average life spans. Large organisms reach reproductive maturity more slowly, have greater generation times, and live longer. This rough correlation depends on the operation of natural selection. *Fitness* of an individual, as stated above, is measured in the final analysis by the individual's contribution to future generations in the number of offspring it produces or fosters in the rest of its race. It is the ability to reproduce, for the continued existence of the population, that really counts. Longevity of the individual is important only insofar as it contributes to the survival of the population. A worker bee, which lives a matter of weeks, doesn't itself produce offspring, but by feeding the queen (which lives years) and rearing her young it contributes to the fitness of the race.

Assume that two individuals live equal lengths of time and both produce two offspring in their lifetimes; but one of them, A, does so twice as early as the other, B. A's progeny will be reaching reproductive maturity about the time that B's are being born. A will have four descendants by the time B has two. It follows that (1) short generation time favors rapid buildup of populations, and (2) physiological adaptation or well-being of the individual is of importance to the population only during the time that that individual is bearing young or directly assisting in their survival. The second consequence helps explain death. After contributing to the reproduction of the race, the individual may be of no selective advantage; it may actually be a disadvantage to the race. If so, there will be no selection for his continued physiological well-being; hence he will age and die. This is illustrated by annual plants in which senescence sets in after seeds begin to develop. (It is an old trick of gardeners to remove flowers from their plants to prolong blooming and life.) Since seeds are the only structure by which the population can endure coming unfavorable environmental conditions, the physiology of the organism becomes devoted entirely to producing seeds, and no energy is wasted on needless vetegative development.

Medawar, an English biologist, has carried this line of reasoning to its logical conclusion: even if we assume that A and B will die only from accident rather than physiological aging, their relative contribution to the reproduction of the race will diminish exponentially with time, because they will rapidly be outnumbered by younger reproducing individuals in a growing population. Health and vitality will be of greater adaptive significance and will be selected more intensively in younger individuals because the latter contribute more to the fitness of the population.

The correlation between size, generation time, and longevity is only a rough one. Much depends on the specific complex of attributes that leads to adaptation. Many herbivores are much larger than man, yet they reproduce earlier and do not live so long. This may be because their inherent length of life is determined by the durability of their teeth. Man lives a very long time compared to other animals. This longevity may be a consequence of his slow development, which slows down his generation time, and also his small litter size (usually one), which requires him to reproduce over a long period in order to maintain his numbers. The reasoning goes like this: it takes a long time to develop a complex body and mind and to charge that mind with tradition and experience. But this development leads eventually to a highly successful organism. For the population to reproduce, however, it has been necessary to evolve a longer period of physiological and reproductive activity.

When an organism occupies a stable environment—take man or forest trees, for example—it may achieve large numbers even though it reproduces slowly. When, however, it lives in transient environments such as old fields or temporary ponds, it can reach large numbers only by having a short generation time and a large number of offspring, or both. And large numbers it *must* reach in order to survive, because it must produce enough seeds to ensure dispersal to new, more suitable environments. A giant *Sequoia* may take 100 years to mature reproductively; a weed or unicellular alga must reproduce in weeks or months before conditions become unsuitable for growth.

Dispersal

Reproduction is necessary for dispersal. Dispersal permits colonizing of new areas with consequent increase of total population size and decrease of the possibility that some chance calamity will wipe out the entire population. Small numbers run a risk of extinction much greater than large numbers dispersed over a greater geographical range or range of habitats.

So it is that all organisms must reproduce. Whether they do so by sexual or asexual means, or both, depends on environmental conditions and the organism's adaptation to them.

FITNESS, ENVIRONMENTAL CHANGE, AND GENETIC SYSTEM

Fitness, we have already seen, is essential to the future existence of the race. Obviously an organism must be adapted morphologically and physiologically to the conditions of existence on an individual basis before it is qualified to reproduce. Adaptation is simpler for organisms living in constant environments like the sea. There, conditions of temperature, salinity, light, and moisture are more or less constantly favorable. Many of these conditions fluctuate widely both seasonally and diurnally on land. Terrestrial organisms have come into being through the evolution of special morphological attributes— for example, vascular tissue, stomata, and cuticle in higher land plants—and regulatory mechanisms that tend to preserve the constancy of the internal environment.

Such organisms also adapt to fluctuating conditions through their ability to develop structures of different form under different environmental conditions (as, for example, the developmental flexibility of the aquatic buttercup, discussed in Chapter 6). These capabilities confer on the individual immediate adaptation to present ranges of environmental conditions. If the environment were never to change there would be no need for change in the organism. However, it does change, and for organisms to be fit over vast stretches of time they have to change and adapt to the new conditions. This involves a genetic change—in other words, organic evolution. Organisms have to balance immediate adaptation against the requirement for evolutionary flexibility. They do so by means of adjustments in their *genetic systems*. Genetic system is the complex of factors interacting to bring about reproduction (genesis) of the population.

Some plants and animals reproduce only by mitotic cell divisions. Lacking any form of sexuality, they have no means of recombination. Mutation is their sole source of variation; thus their genetic system is simple.

Genetic systems that involve sexuality have variation from two sources: mutation and recombination. They are complex and may have several factors regulating the rate of recombination: chromosome number, crossing-over, forced outbreeding, and others. We will examine various genetic systems and their evolution in the following pages.

8

ASEXUAL

REPRODUCTION

OR APOMIXIS

Reproduction is asexual (apomictic) when it occurs without recombination. *Apomixis* (Greek *apo* = without, *mixis* = mingling) is the general term for it. The simplest case is found in unicellular plants and animals where there is doubling of cytoplasmic contents and replication of genetic material followed by division of the cell into two parts. Most reproduction in bacteria, blue-green algae, unicellular algae, and protozoa takes place in this way. These organisms may form resistant cells with dense cytoplasm replete with food reserves and with heavy protective cell wall. These cells permit the species to endure unfavorable conditions and frequently effect dispersal. Multicellular plants may also reproduce by single cells that have been formed by mitotic divisions (mitospores). Sometimes they are flagellated and actively disperse. Sometimes they are resistant structures. Flagellated mitospores occur only in plants that inhabit rivers, ponds, lakes, ocean, watery surface-films, or the watery medium of a host in which they live. Many algae and algal-like fungi (Phycomycetes) have flagellated mitospores. Those fungi completely adapted to terrestrial existence—higher Phycomycetes and Ascomycetes—produce nonflagellated mitospores that are passively dispersed in air. These spores are frequently cleaved off at the tips of hyphae and are called by specialized names depending on the group in question. In Ascomycetes and Fungi Imperfecti these are the *conidiospores*.

Reproduction is virtually synonymous with growth in many of these lower organisms. Multicellular fungal mycelia grow and become fragmented, and the fragments form new mycelia; or multicellular bits of algae break off from the parent plant and start new large plants. Sometimes these multicellular reproductive structures are differentiated: lichens produce soredia, and bryophytes, gemmae.

Soredia (Fig. 8-1) are dust-sized clusters of algal cells surrounded

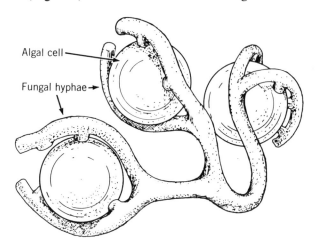

Algal cell

Fungal hyphae

Fig. 8-1. *A lichen soredium.*

by fungal hyphae. They may be formed all over the surface of the lichen body. Doubtless they are critically important in dispersing and maintaining lichen populations, because lichens are dual organisms composed of autotrophic algae and heterotrophic fungi. If the algae and fungi could reproduce only separately, the lichen would have to be reconstituted every time from free-living components—probably a relatively rare event in nature.

Gemmae are lens-shaped packets of cells about a half millimeter long. A dozen or so are formed in little cups on the upper surface of some liverworts. When raindrops fall into these cups, the gemmae are splashed out, and, falling into suitable conditions, they develop into new liverworts.

The open system of growth of nearly all plants lends itself to mitotic vegetative increase. Mosses often have stems that creep along the surface, and upright branches develop from them. In this way a mat is formed. Or a strawberry plant (Fig. 8-2) forms horizontal aerial stems (called *stolons*) that arch up and away from the parent shoot and then down to the soil again, where they strike root and form a new shoot. This process is repeated at each new shoot until the plant has spread out octopus-like over a considerable area.

Fig. 8-2. *Asexual reproduction by stolons in the strawberry.*

Blackberries and many other plants do the same thing, although their stems often may not be so specialized for the purpose. The taking root of branches is like the nurseryman's process of layering: a side branch is covered with a little soil, and roots form where it is covered.

Some plants send out underground stems (*rhizomes*) or roots from which aerial shoots arise. This is especially common in grasses, where the process may go on for so long that single plants come to occupy hundreds of square feet. Such single plants may be broken up into a large number of independent individuals, but all the individuals are genetically identical. They form what is called a *clone*. Clones are common in species that naturally reproduce asexually; they are even more common in agricultural and horticultural plants. There are three main reasons: (1) frequently it takes much less time to grow a mature plant from a cutting or a sucker than from seed; (2) when an especially cherished form reproduces sexually its progeny will usually be inferior because of recombination (unless it habitually self-fertilizes); (3) numerous useful species never set seed and can only be propagated asexually (vegetatively).

Underground runners occur in a few trees (aspen, for instance), in some bad weeds (Canada thistle, *Rumex acetosella,* and bindweed—morning glory), and even in many of the higher fungi that decompose cellulose. In these fungi, mycelia aggregate into strands and also (in *Armillaria mellea,* a Basidiomycete, for example) form near-root-like strands called *rhizomorphs,* which are the thickness of twine and are covered by a black rind and a mucilaginous layer. These structures permit the fungus to traverse regions where individual thread-like hyphae could not survive, and they allow it to muster sufficient reserves at one place for the invasion of new substrate.

Vascular plants have many other mitotically produced multicellular structures for reproduction: aerial bulbils are formed by some (tiger lilies, for example) in leaf axils. They are no more than short, fat stems surrounded by fleshy leaves; they fall as a whole from the parent plant. Underground bulbs are morphologically equivalent to bulbils and are also common agents of asexual reproduction. An onion is a bulb. Another plant that produces bulbs is *Oxalis pescaprae,* the Bermuda buttercup, a native of Africa. It cannot set seed (although it has a large, yellow flower), yet it has become widely established as a weed in California. Corms and tubers are other forms of modified underground stems.

Dahlias and sweet potatoes (morning-glory family) are examples of plants that produce fleshy storage roots that may serve to propagate their species vegetatively. Some plants produce new plantlets on leaves. These drop off and root immediately. This behavior is relatively common in succulents and ferns. Finally, the very plant itself may break up, each portion sending out roots to form a new plant. This happens in cactus and many flowering aquatic plants.

Seeds and fruits, usually regarded as agents of sexual reproduction, have repeatedly evolved into purely asexual structures: an egg cell may be formed in a gametophyte which itself has derived from an unreduced diploid cell. It may then develop into an embryo without fertilization. This is called *diploid parthenogenesis.* Or a diploid cell of the nucellus (ovule tissue enveloping the megagametophyte) may become meristematic, grow into the egg sac, and develop into an embryo either in the absence or presence of normal fertilization. Sometimes, however, pollination is necessary to stimulate growth of an asexually produced embryo. Dandelions provide the most familiar example of asexual production of seeds. They unfailingly set seeds regardless of weather conditions. They illustrate again the common occurrence of apomixis in weeds and the diverse ways in which it is achieved. Asexuality is not limited to plants and protozoa. Parthenogenesis is fairly common in rotifers, lower crustacea, and insects. Aphids may reproduce asexually in warm summer months and sexually at the end of summer. In a warm greenhouse they will continue asexual. So they, like many plants, are facultatively asexual. Obligate asexuality is more common in plants than animals.

ADAPTIVENESS OF ASEXUAL REPRODUCTION

An algal spore lands in a glass of water; a weed lands in a road cut or some barren arctic waste; an aphid is introduced into a crop. These situations have in common a transient environment or transient growing season. The individual organisms must grow and reproduce within a restricted time and must give rise to enough propagules to assure a high probability of the population's survival. Species that occupy transient environments frequently meet the need for rapid increase by asexual reproduction. And those that live in habitats where conditions preclude sexuality (shortness of season or absence of pollinators, for example) *must* have asexual reproduction even if the habitat endures for years (the arctic waste may last but the seasons there are short). This is why so many weeds and pioneers and arctic and alpine plants are asexual.

Some habitats are unstable and therefore unsuitable for seedling establishment. A particularly good example is the shifting sand dune, where vegetative reproduction, especially by stolons and rhizomes, is unusually common. On the shifting sands of the Oregon coast, common pioneer plants are two kinds of beach grass and several species of rush—all rhizome-forming; sand verbena, strawberry, and kinnikinnick (bearberry) are dicotyledonous plants whose stems run along the surface or under the sand. Vegetative reproduction permits these species, once established, to radiate out and also survive inundation by sand. All these plants have a role in ecological succession because they stabilize the sand and make it suitable for germination of other species that eventually replace them.

Ecological succession is the flow of populations from the first opening of a habitat to achievement of a more or less stable dynamic equilibrium. It occurs because the organisms work changes in the environment that render it unsuitable to themselves or more suitable to other organisms. Pioneers of the earliest stages of a terrestrial system are bacteria, blue-green algae, lichens, mosses, and vascular plants usually with small, easily dispersed propagules. It is interesting to note that along with physiological and morphological adaptations to such environments, these organisms frequently reproduce asexually. Small size, short generation time, dispersability, asexuality, and rapid population increase go hand in hand and fit them for their lives as pioneers. We shall see later that self-fertilization in sexual forms can meet many of the qualifications of asexuality, and many pioneer species are both sexual and capable of self-fertilization.

EVOLUTIONARY CONSEQUENCES OF ASEXUALITY

Asexuality permits rapid increase of genotypes that are well suited to prevailing conditions, and it is a means of preserving particularly well-adapted genomes instead of letting them be segregated and recombined. In other words, there is no risk that the progeny will be ill-adapted because of recombination away from a combination of genes giving good adaptation. This is fine, but what happens if there is a change in the environment? The organism will not be able to evolve new adaptive gene combinations through the rapid means of recombination. Mutation becomes the only route of evolution.

Perhaps this is not so serious for unicellular organisms, which exist in astronomical numbers. Mutants do arise. For instance, antibiotic-resistant bacteria have arisen by mutation in experiments designed to detect them. As generation time increases, however, and the number of individuals decreases more and more, reliance must be placed on genetic systems that permit or even demand recombination. Where is there a large tree or higher animal that is obligately asexual? Some smaller trees such as aspen or alder do reproduce asexually, but they also have sexual reproduction. Where asexuality does exist in trees it is usually associated with adaptation to extreme environments. It allows for local increase of a given genotype. Whole aspen groves may form a clone of individuals all derived by vegetative runners from one starting individual. Sod-forming grasses do the same thing, and single clones have been found which cover hundreds of square feet.

In summary, we might say that obligate asexuality is an evolutionary blind alley, especially in organisms with long generation times.

9

RECOMBINATION

AND SEXUAL

REPRODUCTION

Since, as we have seen, reproduction can occur without sexuality, you might ask, "Can sex take place without reproduction?" The answer is "Yes," if you consider sex to be equivalent to recombination. Usually we think of sex as involving two main processes: meiosis in a diplophase, and fusion of haploid gametes. Then, indeed, we can speak of sexual reproduction, and recombination of genes is its principal consequence. But recombination of genes can occur in ways that don't necessarily result in reproduction. Most such recombination goes on in lowly forms, such as viruses, bacteria, and molds. Complex plants and animals can recombine genes only by means of old-fashioned sex.

SEXUALITY IN PROKARYOTES

Avery, MacLeod, and McCarty *transformed* a pneumococcus from nonpathogenic to pathogenic by growing it in the presence of DNA of a killed pathogenic strain (see Chapter 5). They made a new combination of genes. A few years later Lederberg and Tatum proved that certain bacteria display recombination naturally by performing the following experiment. The colon bacterium, *Escherichia coli,* will grow on a simple minimal medium of nutrients. Mutant strains that require additional vitamins, however, arise. Two such mutant strains were selected, one that needed biotin and methionine and another that needed threonine and leucine. These strains would not grow alone on a medium lacking these compounds, but when the bacteria were mixed together and plated out on such a medium, over a hundred colonies appeared. This meant that over one hundred recombining events had occurred in which the synthetically active genes of one strain joined those of the other.

This discovery has been verified by remarkable electron-micro-photographs showing two bacterial cells lying side by side, with one injecting the other with its strand of DNA. Genes are transferred only in one direction from a donor to a recipient cell, and through this process, known as *bacterial conjugation,* recombination can occur. Note that recombination is not linked to reproduction. Normal syngamy and meiosis do not take place. This is perhaps related to the fact that bacteria (and blue-green algae) do not have typical chromosomes situated inside well-defined nuclear membranes. For this reason they are classed together as *Prokaryota.*

Bacteria are attacked by viruses in the same way as are man, tobacco, and peaches. "Bacteria-eating" viruses (bacteriophages) are now known to be molecular complexes of protein and DNA or RNA. One of these bacteriophages invades a bacterial cell and causes the bacterial genes to copy the genetic code in the virus's DNA instead of its own. Thus, hundreds of new virus particles are formed and eventually released when the infected bacterial cell ruptures. Bacteriophages that behave this way are termed *virulent.*

Sometimes what are known as *temperate bacteriophages* enter the host cell. They do not cause its early destruction by initiating synthesis of new phage nucleic acid and protein. Instead, the phage nucleic acid becomes associated with the bacterial genetic material. It may stay in this benign state for generations of bacterial cells, during which its nucleic acid is replicated along with the bacteria's. The bacterium usually does not show signs of the presence of the virus; however, on occasion, the phage permanently alters the behavior or properties of the bacterium. For example, the diphtheria-causing bacterium can only produce diphtheria toxin when it is infected with a phage.

On rare occasions, the benign phage particles become virulent and cause phage replication. During this replication, bacterial DNA may become attached to the phages, so that when they are released and reinfect other bacteria, they carry over (i.e. *transduce*) to them new bacterial genes. These genes, in turn, may be incorporated into the bacterial DNA. In this way novel combinations of bacterial DNA are formed. This bacteriophage-mediated recombination is known as *transduction,* to distinguish it from transformation and bacterial conjugation.

The reader who is interested in a more detailed discussion of bacterial and viral reproduction and sexuality will find a lucid treatment in the book by Stanier et al. cited in the references at the end of this book.

These discoveries in bacterial recombination have made possible the wonderful recent advances in knowledge of the molecular structure of the gene, and of how it carries the genetic message. They have also changed our concept of the evolutionary importance of recombination: although reproduction is asexual in bacteria and viruses, recombination can occur in them. This fact suggests that recombination may be nearly as fundamental to existence as replication and mutation themselves.

SEXUALITY IN EUKARYOTES

Origin of Meiosis

There are many unicellular animal and plant flagellates that are eukaryotes (have typical chromosomes and nucleus) but in which no one has ever been able to find syngamy or meiosis. On the whole they are the simpler forms: *Protococcus* and *Cryptophyceae*. There thus seems to be a congruence between absence of sex and simplicity of architecture. Whether recombination never occurs or never has existed in them is uncertain. Nevertheless, meiosis and syngamy apparently arose subsequent to evolution of chromosomes. We speak of *the* origin of chromosomes and meiosis; yet, is it not possible— given the apparent evolutionary value of recombination—that they arose independently a number of times?

Evolutionary Trend in Duration of Diplophase

Many of the most primitive unicellular or filamentous algae and protozoa have *haplontic* life cycles. Increase in numbers is largely by asexual mitotic divisions. Under proper environmental conditions, syngamy may occur: two cell bodies fuse (plasmogamy) and their nuclei then fuse (karyogamy), forming a diploid zygote. In some species this cell becomes a resistant spore to tide the organism over hard times. In any case the next cell division is meiotic, and four haploid daughter cells usually result (Fig. 9-1). Two genomes make fleeting contact, associate, and exchange material; recombination is possible.

The life cycle of most multicellular algae and higher plants differs slightly and significantly from this scheme. We call it *haplo-diplontic,* for instead of the zygote's dividing immediately *meiotically,* it starts

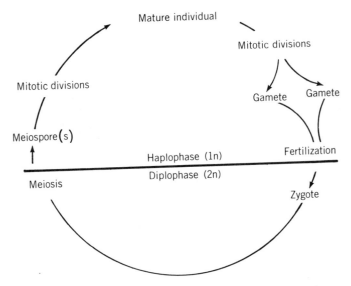

Fig. 9-1. *Haplontic life cycle as found in many simple algae.*

dividing *mitotically*. The parent genomes stay together awhile and produce many diploid cells which usually remain together in some complex multicellular structure (organism). Then after some time, certain cells enter meiosis and produce haploid cells (meiospores). These latter then multiply mitotically, separating or remaining together to form a multicellular structure. Eventually two of them behave as gametes and form a zygote (Fig. 6-8).

Evolution has gone, on the whole, from the simple to the complex. This amounts to saying that evolution has involved differentiation: differentiation among vegetative cells of one or both phases, morphological differentiation between the phases, and differentiation between gametes. In the simplest cases gametes look alike and resemble meiospores, and haplophase looks like diplophase. In the most complex, gametes are differentiated into egg and sperm and differ greatly from meiospores; haplophase and diplophase also differ greatly.

In many algae and all vascular plants, the diplophase is larger and more durable than the haplophase. In Chapter 6 we discussed the life cycles of a fern (Fig. 6-9), a gymnosperm (Fig. 6-10), and an angiosperm (Fig. 6-11), and observed in them a progressive reduction in size and duration of the gametophyte. Indeed, in flowering plants all that you see of the haplophase is the pollen and—hidden deep inside protective diploid tissues, scarcely visible with the naked eye—the egg sac (Fig. 6-11). Thus, in the course of evolution of haplo-diplontic vascular plants, there has been a reduction in the haplophase.

A few brown and green algae and all animals above protozoa (and some of them, too) have *diplontic* life cycles. The zygote divides mitotically and develops into a multicellular organism. Some of its cells enter meiosis and produce meiospores, which, instead of dividing mitotically to form a haplophase, behave as gametes, and fuse and form a zygote. The haplophase has been reduced to the duration of a single cell (see Fig. 6-7). This is just contrary to the haplontic life cycle; all cells except the gametes have two genomes associated in them.

Well, you may ask, why stop there? Why not triploid and higher numbers? In fact there are approaches to such conditions. Flowering plants have polyploid endosperm; and ascomycetous fungi may have cells with three different kinds of nuclei in them.

An explanation of why the diplophase (diploid state) has gained ascendancy over haplophase (haploid state) is presented at length in the next chapter.

ECOLOGICAL CONSEQUENCES OF SEXUALITY

Reproduction by sexuality requires a chain of events all of which are equally important, but if we had to choose, no doubt we would select fertilization (syngamy) as the most interesting link, if not also the most important. So much of life's form and behavior centers around fertilization: the fabulous contrivances of flowers to attract insects, which carry pollen from anthers to style; the remarkable plumage and courting behavior of male birds; the subtle psychological forces that bring together man and woman—these are just a few of the obvious means evolved to ensure the fusion of gametes.

Nondirected Movement of Fertilizing Agents

Red algae have no flagellated cells. Sperms or microgametes, as they are called, are produced in enormous numbers and are passively carried to eggs in water currents. Like so much dust floating in the sea, the cells resemble pollen grains (microgametophytes) floating in air currents. Produced in clouds, usually around the time of the vernal and autumnal equinoxes, from pendant anthers of grasses or catkins and strobili of trees, pollen is carried passively until, by chance, it is enmeshed in a feather-like style or caught in a drop of liquid at the mouth of a gymnosperm's ovule. Surely this is a wasteful means for achieving syngamy, but it works. At least the plant is independent of other organisms.

Directed Movement of Fertilizing Agents

Directed movement toward some goal requires that there be some stimulus, a receptor of the stimulus, and an effector for movement. All eukaryotic algae (except reds), most phycomycetous fungi, all bryophytes, and all vascular cryptogams have flagellated sperm that find their way from a gametangium or antheridium to a free-floating egg, a female gametangium, or an archegonium. Substances (hormones) have been isolated from the female gametangia of two thallophytes (the water mold, *Allomyces,* and a green alga, *Oedogonium*), and from the archegonia of ferns, which stimulate the flagellated sperms to swim toward them.

Higher Phycomycetes, Ascomycetes, and Basidiomycetes lack flagellated cells; directed movement is achieved in them by growth of a "male" hypha to an enlarged passive "female" hypha. The latter cell secretes an attractant hormone (see *Achlya,* Chapter 6). This stimulus by diffusible chemicals in lower plants is reminiscent of diffusible substances given off by female moths to attract males from great distances, or perhaps of perfumes diffusing from attractive female humans.

Land plants are fixed in place. When they are not self-fertilizing, movement of gamete-bearing structures must, if directed at all, be by means of some animal agent. The better part of flower evolution has been devoted to effecting syngamy. All conceivable sensitivities of insects have been exploited by flowering plants: pollen and nectar have been offered as food, color and odor have been used to lure them, even their reproductive instincts have been taken advantage of. But birds, bats, and slugs have also been used to bear pollen from one flower to another. Much of flower and insect evolution can be regarded as an evolving symbiotic relationship that has increased the effectiveness of cross-fertilization in flowering plants.

Sexuality places some restriction on reproduction of a species. We noted in Chapter 8 that rapid population increase is achieved more easily asexually, because sex may take more time. Furthermore, unless an organism is bisexual and self-fertile, it takes two—a male and a female—to reproduce. Hence, unisexual organisms will be at a disadvantage in colonizing new territories. For instance, if the chance of dispersal and establishment of one individual under a given set of conditions is .1, the chance for two concurrently is $.1 \times .1 = .01$, and the chance for male and female concurrently is $.1 \times .1 \times .5 = .005$.

10

CONTROL OF

RECOMBINATION

AND EVOLUTION

OF GENETIC

SYSTEMS

COMPLEMENTATION AND OTHER GENETIC
CONSEQUENCES OF DIPLOIDY

Why, we must ask, has there been an evolution toward diploidy and away from haploidy? For one reason, because complementation is enhanced by diploidy. When Bateson, Punnett, and Saunders crossed two white-flowered sweet peas and produced a purple-flowered one, they showed that two different genomes, both incapable of carrying a reaction to completion, might do so when brought together in the same cytoplasm. We saw this phenomenon again in the experiment by the Marchals, where the diploid moss gametophyte was bisexual whereas the haploid was unisexual. Still another case is from Esser and Straub's study of the Ascomycete *Sordaria:* self-sterile mutants of a normally self-fertile strain would form normal fruiting structures and spores when nuclei from different self-sterile mutants were brought together in the same cell by plasmogamy. This sort of complementation is known as *heterokaryotic vigor.* A *homo-karyon* is an ascomycetous or basidiomycetous mycelium with just one kind of haploid nucleus in it. Mycelia of different homokaryons may fuse and their two kinds of nuclei intermingle. They may migrate and multiply at different rates throughout old and new vegetative hyphae (especially in Ascomycetes). But that doesn't matter; there are still two kinds of nuclei present. The mycelium is called a *heterokaryon.*

Discovery of heterokaryotic vigor began in 1942 when an American, Dodge, took a homokaryotic dwarf strain, which had been produced by X-irradiation, and made a heterokaryon between it and a slow-growing, otherwise normal strain. The heterokaryon grew faster than either homokaryotic parent! Later workers were able to make heterokaryons grow on a medium on which neither homokaryotic parent would grow. The parent nuclei had genes for different parts of a biosynthetic sequence; when placed together they complemented one another. This can be diagrammed as follows:

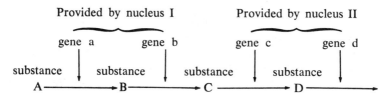

In this case, each nucleus was deficient for genes mediating a different biochemical transformation within a single biosynthetic pathway. However, complementation can also be said to occur when each nucleus provides genes for a complete but different synthetic pathway. For example, a strain of the Ascomycete *Neurospora* exists that is unable to carry out all the steps in the synthesis of the amino acid tryptophane. Hence it requires tryptophane in its growth medium. Another strain occurs that cannot synthesize the amino acid arginine, and that consequently requires that arginine be added to its growth medium. When a heterokaryon is formed from these two nuclear types, however, it can grow without either added tryptophane or arginine. The heterokaryon can synthesize both compounds.

Complementation is one result of diploidy; concealed variability is another. A diploid may carry many recessive genes whose effects are seldom expressed from generation to generation. When they are, they may result in lowered fitness to the prevailing environment. If the environment should change, however, the recessives might just confer greater fitness than the dominants that masked them and permit survival of the population. Thus diploidy makes possible storing up genetic variability as protection against environmental change. It allows for evolution instead of annihilation.

Ability to cope with changes by genetic evolution has been termed evolutionary flexibility. It is favored by diploidy, mutation, and recombination (sexuality). But these latter processes may at the same time work against the adjustment of the organism to the here and now. If an organism is well-suited to an environment and its reproduction involves recombination, its offspring may not be as well-suited as it, because they will have genomes that differ from it according to the extent of recombination. There is thus a basic conflict between *evolutionary flexibility* and *immediate fitness*. We shall see later how forces favoring the one or the other balance out under different ecological circumstances.

EFFECTS OF INBREEDING AND OUTBREEDING

We learned from Johannsen's experiments that successive inbreeding produces homozygosity and pure lines. If we begin with a heterozygous individual (AaBb) and let it and its offspring inbreed for several generations, several pure lines will result: AABB, AAbb, aaBB, and aabb. There is a tendency toward generation of four phenotypes instead of one. Similar chance fixation of alleles can take place even in outbreeders when their populations are very small (100 or less). This divergence of populations due to inbreeding or reduction in population size is called *genetic drift*. The opposite effect, achieved by hybridization, is a swamping of differences, a tendency to keep the population more or less uniformly heterozygous.

A second effect of inbreeding is known as *inbreeding depression*. Darwin discovered it by artificially self-pollinating numerous flowering plants. Thriftiness and fertility decreased with each successive inbred generation. The phenomenon is well-known from animal breeding, and is most likely to be observed in obligately outbreeding organisms. Evidently, balanced development in them has come to depend on the complementation provided by heterozygosity at many loci. The opposite of inbreeding depression is *hybrid vigor,* or heterosis. It is manifest as increased thriftiness and fertility of hybrid progeny in contrast to those of the parents. Development of hybrid corn is but one example of how man has taken advantage of this effect.

Thus, inbreeding and outbreeding have opposite effects. Inbreeding favors pure lines whose progeny will resemble their parents and will likely be suited to the same environment. In this regard inbreeding comes to promote immediate fitness at the expense of flexibility, and resembles asexuality. Outbreeding favors a great store of variability: individuals will be highly heterozygous and progeny will differ from parents. It promotes evolutionary flexibility possibly at the expense of immediate fitness.

FACTORS AFFECTING RECOMBINATION

The balance between coherence and recombination of genetic factors is maintained by the genetic system, which has components at three levels: chromosome, organism, and population. In the following we will see how these affect recombination.

If an organism is unisexual, obviously it cannot self-fertilize and inbreed directly. If it is bisexual or bisporic it still may not be able to self-fertilize for many reasons: (1) there may be a gene-controlled physiological incompatibility mechanism that prevents fusion of gametes or growth of pollen tube in a style; (2) sperm or pollen may ripen or be shed at different times than eggs or styles so as to be temporally isolated; (3) sex cells may be spatially kept apart in separate flowers (*monoecy*) or within the confines of one flower by its peculiar morphology (as, for example, in orchids).

Even though an organism cannot self-fertilize, inbreeding may occur through matings among sibs or sibs and parents. The smaller the breeding population, the more likely that inbreeding will occur; and, as a corollary to this, the less the dispersal of adults or seeds or pollen, the smaller the interbreeding population. Coherence of genetic factors will also be favored by lower chromosome number, by reduction in crossover frequency, and by inversions and translocations.

All these mechanisms have been exploited in the adaptation of plants and animals to their environments. Organisms, such as weeds, living in unfavorable, transient environments frequently have devices for ensuring immediate fitness. Rapid population rise is most favored where the maximum number of offspring closely resembles the parents, which have demonstrated ability to survive in the habitat. But we have seen that coherence achieved through inbreeding can lead to depression. Several ways of getting around this have evolved. One of the most common in plants is *allopolyploidy:* two quite distinct diploid genomes are brought together. No matter how much the plant is inbred, there is bound to remain the heterozygosity conferred by the initial difference in genomes. Many self-pollinating weeds and cultivated plants are polyploid.

Long-lived organisms of stable habitats and constant population size usually have a genetic system that favors recombination. Forest trees may set seeds for centuries before one of them finally germinates, strikes roots into the soil, and survives. The tree population can try out an enormous number of gene combinations without jeopardizing its existence. Ability to improve adaptation to the present conditions and to change genetically in harmony with changes in the environment both become of paramount adaptive significance to the population.

We have now seen that the genetic system itself has great adaptive significance, and for this reason it, too, will evolve along with physiology and morphology in the adaptation of organisms to new conditions. It can be illustrated by an example from the fungi and some general comments from the angiosperms.

EVOLUTION OF GENETIC SYSTEM IN TRUE FUNGI

Evolution in fungi is an enormously complex subject, and it is possible here to give only a broad idea of the course of evolution, and to show that evolution involves changes in genetic system as well as form and function.

Phycomycetes are coenocytic filamentous or unicellular organisms that live as saprophytes or parasites in aquatic and terrestrial environments. The gametes of aquatic species have flagella and are differentiated into eggs and sperm, while in terrestrial forms the sex cells (called gametangia) have no flagella. They may, however, still be morphologically differentiated into a larger oogonium and smaller antheridium (as, for example, *Achlya,* discussed in Chapter 6). In some of the most strictly terrestrial forms, such as *Rhizopus* (bread mold), there is no morphological difference in sex organs. Rapid population increase through asexual means is by motile mitospores in species adapted to aquatic or semiaquatic habitats and by airborne conidiospores in those completely adapted to terrestrial existence. Phycomycetes may be regarded as primitive nutritionally, for they can decompose only simple carbohydrates; only a few decompose cellulose. Their hyphal walls are composed of cellulose and chitin.

Most Phycomycetes have haplontic life cycles, although a few have haplo-diplontic cycles. Bisexuality (monoecy) and self-compatibility are common; in other words, self-fertilization can occur, and, when it does, homozygosity is immediately established, since both gametes come from the same haploid.

Self-incompatibility has arisen in a few groups and is controlled by two alleles at one locus. That is, there are plus (A_1) and minus (A_2) strains, and for two gametes or gametangia to fuse they must carry contrasting alleles. Thus, self-mating is impossible, and when two individuals meet there will be a 50-50 chance that they will be able to copulate and recombine genes. It does not, however, prevent matings between sibs of opposite allelic type, which will be produced in 1 : 1 proportion at meiosis. Consequently, inbreeding may occur rather easily.

Ascomycetes are mainly terrestrial. They differ morphologically from Phycomycetes in having cross-septations in their hyphae; but there is a pore in each septum which permits passage of nuclei. Their hyphal walls are composed mainly of chitin. The most constant feature of the group is the *meiosporangium* or *ascus,* which is a sac-like cell where nuclear fusion and meiosis both occur. Flagellated cells do not occur in Ascomycetes. Many Ascomycetes are parasitic, but they are perhaps even more important as cellulose decomposers. They number around 12,500 species, whereas there are about 1,300 Phycomycetes.

Ascomycetous reproduction and nuclear cycles are quite complex. Dimorphism of gametes is unknown, although gametangia may differ. The basic scheme is as follows: two uninucleate mycelia develop, which, if compatible, develop gametangia that fuse (plasmogamy). Nuclei of the two parental types pair (but do not fuse) and divide synchronously to form a binucleate (dikaryotic) mycelium. This produces asci, wherein nuclear pairs fuse (karyogamy). The zygote immediately divides meiotically. Usually each meiospore divides once mitotically so that eight ascospores are formed. The ascospore is released and, finding suitable conditions, germinates to form a new uninucleate mycelium. Thus, strictly speaking, the life cycle is haplontic. But there is a complication: vegetative hyphae may fuse (plasmogamy) and nuclei of two (sometimes more) types intermingle in a single mycelium without fusing. The proportions of nuclei may vary widely, environmental conditions selecting now for the one, now the other type. As two or more nuclear types are present, there exists a *heterokaryon.* This heterokaryon shows complementation and heterokaryotic vigor, as described earlier. In fact, it mimics diploidy. Yet it isn't as rigid a condition; nuclear migration and differential rates of nuclear division make possible variation in the dose of the genomes. Also, immediate fitness is enhanced by fusions of vegetative hyphae of many different genomes. Many different nuclear combinations can be tried out and adjustments made to the environment *within* a given generation. There is the difficulty, however, common to sexual organisms, that the well-fit heterokaryon will be recombined out of existence by nuclear fusion (karyogamy) and meiosis. This can be circumvented in some species by production of binucleate asexual spores—in other words, heterokaryotic coni-diospores.

Self-*in*compatibility is much more frequent in Ascomycetes than in Phycomycetes. Usually it is under control of the one-locus–two-allele system known as *bipolar control*. As in Phycomycetes, this system prevents self-fertilization of the haploid and permits out-crossing with half of the population, but it does not restrict crossing between sibs. Yet inbreeding through sib matings and self-fertilization in those that are self-compatible do not inevitably reduce variability, because heterokaryons can be formed. Indeed, self-compatible strains can heterokaryotize without restriction.

It is apparent that recombination of nuclei through heterokary-ons could go far to substitute for recombination through karyo-gamy and meiosis. The Fungi Imperfecti, or Deuteromycetes, are an artificial class of fungi, rich in species and important in the economy of nature. But they do not form meiosporangia and therefore—although they look vegetatively like Ascomycetes or Basidiomycetes and form abundant conidiospores—they cannot easily be classified. They appear to lack sexuality. In fact, however, they have nuclear recombination by somatic fusion of hyphae and formation of hetero-karyons. The nuclei act as linkage groups, with an important and surprising exception. Recombination of chromosomal material can occur through a process known as *parasexuality* (which, by the way, is also known in the true Ascomycetes and Basidiomycetes). It comes about first by fusion of unlike nuclei of a heterokaryon. The fusion nucleus divides mitotically, and occasionally crossing-over occurs be-tween homologous chromosomes. Now and then chromosome num-ber is reduced to the haploid level and new strains sort out. Classical sex has been circumvented altogether: no differentiated sex cells and their fusion, no normal meiosis. Heterokaryosis, parasexuality, and asexual spores constitute a genetic system that permits recombina-tion, perhaps at a lower rate than by normal sexual mechanisms, but without restriction on interfertility imposed by incompatibility systems.

Basidiomycetes are exclusively terrestrial fungi. Many live as para-sites, but most familiar mushrooms and bracket fungi are decom-posers of cellulose and lignin. They are the only fungi able to decompose lignin and thus may be regarded as most advanced bio-chemically. Structurally they resemble Ascomycetes in having septate hyphae; by and large, however, nuclear migration does not occur across septae. The meiosporangium develops in much the same way as the ascus, but mitotic divisions don't take place after meiosis, and the meiospores migrate out into pockets at the tip of the meiosporangium and are pinched off. Whereas Ascomycetes may have a vegetative heterokaryon phase with indefinite proportion of unlike nuclei, Basidiomycetes have just two nuclei per cell in this phase (dikaryophase). Fusion of vegetative cells or specialized gametangia (plasmogamy) occurs when they are of compatible mating type. This fusion brings together two unlike nuclei, which then proceed to divide synchronously, and cell division is structured to assure the constancy of the nuclear ratio at 1 : 1. In many Basidiomycetes, the dikaryophase is the dominant phase of the life cycle—that is, of relatively greatest duration. Karyogamy and meiosis occur in the meiosporangium as they do in the Ascomycetes.

Genetic control of mating type is quite complex in Basidiomycetes. Self-*in*compatibility is the rule, applying to about 90 per cent of the species. The one-locus–two-allele system occurs, but is less common than the one-locus–multiple-allele system, where instead of there being just two alleles, A_1 and A_2, there are many: A_1, A_2, A_3, ... A_n. We studied this condition in *Nicotiana* (tobacco), having used it to develop the concept of multiple alleles. If there is a sufficiently large number of these alleles in an interbreeding population, the probability of intercompatibility of any two individuals taken at random may approach 99 per cent. This means that the possibility of sexuality is greatly increased. Yet intersib mating is still possible, as in the bipolar control with two alleles, for the two alleles segregate at meiosis and half the meiospores will carry one allele and half the other.

A system of control that reduces inter-sib mating has evolved in the mushrooms. It is called tetrapolar control: there are two loci, the A and the B; plasmogamy can occur only between individuals that are heterozygous at both loci. Hence all zygotes are A_1A_2, B_1B_2 and four types of meiospores are produced: A_1B_1, A_1B_2, A_2B_1, and A_2B_2. Self-mating is obviously out, and matings can take place only between A_1B_1 and A_2B_2 on the one hand, and A_1B_2 and A_2B_1 on the other. Therefore, any one haploid can mate with only one-fourth of the sibs issuing from one parent zygote, and thus the extent of inbreeding between sibs is half that of bipolar systems.

Multiplicity of alleles also occurs in this tetrapolar system, and, as in the bipolar multiple-allele case, probability of successful mating between non-sibs is thereby increased. For instance, if we assumed three alleles at both A and B loci with equal frequency in the population, the probability of intersib mating remains at 1/4, and that for non-sib mating becomes 4/9 (there are nine possible genotypes in the population). Consequently the ratio of outbreeding to inbreeding becomes 4/9 divided by 1/4 = 16/9. Natural populations have more than 25 alleles per locus, so that in them the ratio of outbreeding to inbreeding is yet larger and the probability of intercompatibility of non-sibs approaches unity.

Inbreeding by inter-sib mating is reduced by tetrapolar control. It could conceivably be reduced even further by having three or more loci involved in the control of compatibility; however, a certain amount would always remain possible in the haplontic life cycle. Only by intervention of the diplophase are haplo-diplontic plants able to prevent mating between daughter gametophytes of one parent. We shall see later how this works in the angiosperms.

These higher Basidiomycetes have no specialized asexual spores. Fragments of mycelia may start new colonies, true, but meiospores alone seem to suffice to reproduce and disseminate the species. Sexuality has gained ascendancy. Furthermore, these are the most complex fungi morphologically. Apparently evolution of their complex form has had to await evolution of the heterogenic dikaryon, which provides complementation and at the same time enough integrity of genome to permit the completion of complex developmental sequences. Such stability and integration is not available to the flexible heterokaryon of the Ascomycetes.

There are about 13,500 species of Basidiomycetes—more than in the other classes of fungi. Might not this majority be related to the greater evolutionary potentiality of these sexual organisms with predominantly obligate outbreeding?

SUMMARY OF EVOLUTION OF GENETIC
SYSTEM IN TRUE FUNGI

Evolution in fungi has involved development of remarkable systems favoring immediate fitness and evolutionary flexibility. Immediate fitness is favored by asexual reproduction and heterokaryosis—both important in organisms dispersed as spores and building up large populations from few starting cells. Evolution has freed the organisms from the confines of sexuality based on sexual dimorphism and water-requiring gametes. No longer must there be two morphologically differentiated sexes that restrict probability of syngamy to 50 per cent. In higher Basidiomycetes no morphological differentiation exists. There are many sexes, in that any one individual cannot self-fertilize but can breed with up to about 99 per cent of the rest of the individuals of the species. This has nearly doubled the probability of recombination. At the same time, the probability of inbreeding among sibs has been reduced from one (in self-compatible forms) to one-half (in self-incompatible forms with bipolar control) to one-fourth (in self-incompatible organisms with tetrapolar control).

The Ascomycetes, Basidiomycetes, and Fungi Imperfecti have evolved the possibility of trying out a large number of nuclear combinations through plasmogamy and heterokaryosis. The Basidiomycete has at the same time evolved a means of preserving a stable nuclear ratio. In them, heterokaryotic vigor is achieved without sacrificing integration of synthetic capacity of heterogenic nuclei. Complicated developmental sequences can go to completion because the nuclei remain together in the dikaryon.

It can be said that there has been a trend of increasing complementation. Phycomycetes are haplontic or haplo-diplontic; Ascomycetes have heterokaryons of indefinite duration; but some Basidiomycetes regularly form the heterokaryon soon after germination of the meiospore, so that the organism is heterokaryotic throughout most of its life. This is analogous to the trend toward diploidy from haploidy, which was discussed in the last chapter.

EVOLUTION OF GENETIC SYSTEM IN SEED PLANTS

Genetic systems in seed plants are exceedingly diverse, and trends are not clear-cut. Seed plants differ from fungi in that the significant plant body is universally the diplophase. Nothing like heterokaryosis exists, and asexual reproduction is not by spores.

Many years ago Charles Darwin observed that "nature abhors inbreeding." He had come to this conclusion from a study of flowering plants. Pollen from the flowers of many plants, when placed on the styles of the source flowers or others on the same plant, failed to produce seeds. Most angiosperms are self-incompatible, and the basis for this condition is to be found in the style. The diplophase of the angiosperm has taken control. Recall how if the tobacco diploid bears incompatibility alleles S_1 and S_2 (called A_1 and A_2 for fungi), its own haploid pollen bearing S_1 or S_2 will not grow in its style. Only that pollen which bears other alleles in the multiple-allelic series will do so. The angiosperm has precluded self-mating of haplophase by having the haploid generation unisexual and has precluded any inbreeding of sibling haplophases at all by interposing a single over-riding self-incompatibility by means of diploid tissues. Multiple allely ensures high probability of intercompatibility of any two individuals taken at random. The control is similar to the bipolar multiple-allele system of fungi, but more effectively prevents inbreeding.

Most floral diversity can be explained as adaptation that ensures outbreeding and that increases efficiency of dispersal of pollen. When a plant has to prevent self-pollination by incompatibility at the style, it wastes a good part of its pollen. Orchids and many other plants get around this by having intricate floral configurations that not only attract insects but ensure that no pollen is wasted and none comes into contact with its own style. The insect is exploited. Although the diploid plants can't seek one another out, they do what is next best by having animals do it for them. Gene-controlled self-incompatibility mechanisms have often been lost in them; so every plant is fertile with every other, yet no plant can self-fertilize because of its innate morphology.

Many important angiosperms are self-fertile. Cultivated wheat is a good example, for, not only is it a major crop, but it illustrates a mechanism that prevents depletion of heterozygosity in spite of inbreeding. You will recall that modern wheats are hexaploid—that is, they have in them three different diploid genomes. The basic differences between these genomes will persist regardless of inbreeding. Seed plants that obligately inbreed have frequently escaped inbreeding depression by means of allopolyploidy.

CONCLUSION

Life must reproduce, and reproduce with change, if it is to endure in earth's fluctuating environments. Natural selection favors genetic systems that for given environments yield maximum immediate fitness and evolutionary flexibility. We have seen how manifold are the components of the genetic system: genes, chromosomes, cells, organisms, populations of related organisms, and interactions of unrelated organisms. Is it any wonder that there is such a diversity of genetic systems when so many components can be varied and when there are so many environments on earth? While we wonder at the precision of replication of the genic molecules and their control of cytoplasmic activities, we must be awed by the nicety of adjustment of genetic system and how evolutionary advances in it have set the stage for evolution of greater physiological and morphological complexity and the homeostatic properties they confer.

SUGGESTIONS FOR

FURTHER READING

Alexopoulos, C. J. *Introductory Mycology,* 2nd ed. New York: John Wiley & Sons, Inc., 1962. An authoritative basic reference to the morphology, classification, and biology of fungi.

Comfort, A. *The Biology of Senescence.* London: Routledge and Kegan Paul, 1956. The Introduction and Chapter 1 contain a helpful discussion of the biological significance of longevity.

Crick, F. H. C. "The Genetic Code." *Scientific American,* Vol. 207 (Oct. 1962), pp. 67–72. An article on recent discoveries in molecular genetics by a leading scientist.

Darlington, C. D. *The Evolution of Genetic Systems,* 2nd ed. New York: Basic Books, Inc., 1958. A revised edition of the classic work on genetic systems.

Dobzhansky, T. *Evolution, Genetics and Man.* New York: John Wiley & Sons, Inc., 1955. A lucid elementary textbook of evolution and its genetic basis.

East, E. M., and P. J. Mangelsdorf. "A New Interpretation of the Hereditary Behaviour of Self-Sterile Plants." *Proceedings of the National Academy of Sciences,* 11 (1925), 166–171.

Garrett, S. D. *Soil Fungi and Soil Fertility.* New York: Pergamon Press Inc., 1963. Includes a chapter on genetics of fungi which, together with much fascinating information on fungal ecology, makes this a useful little book.

Mazia, D. "How Cells Divide." *Scientific American,* Vol. 205 (Sept. 1961), pp. 100–108. Reviews the mechanism of mitosis.

Mendel, G. "Versuch über Pflanzenhybriden." *Verhandlungen des Naturforschenden Vereins in Brünn,* Vol. 4 (1865). This classic on "Experiments in Plant Hybridization" is available in the original German and in English translations.

Morgan, T. H., A. H. Sturtevant, H. J. Muller, and C. B. Bridges. *The Mechanism of Mendelian Heredity.* New York: Henry Holt and Company, 1915. A clearly written introduction to genetics by four great American geneticists; gives the reader a feel for the exciting years that followed rediscovery of Mendel's laws.

Nirenberg, M. W. "The Genetic Code II." *Scientific American,* Vol. 208, (Mar. 1963), pp. 80–86. A sequel to Crick's article.

Raper, J. R. "The Control of Sex in Fungi." *American Journal of Botany*, Vol. 47, pp. 794–808. A technical but exhaustive review paper.

Schultz, J. "The Evidence of the Nucleoprotein Nature of the Gene." *Cold Spring Harbor Symposia on Quantitative Biology*, 9 (1941), 55–65.

Srb, A., and R. Owen. *General Genetics*. San Francisco: W. H. Freeman and Company, 1955. A standard genetics textbook.

Stanier, R., M. Doudoroff, and E. Adelberg. *The Microbial World*, 2nd ed. Englewood Cliffs, N. J.: Prentice-Hall, Inc., 1963. This comprehensive work has three chapters on microbial genetics.

Stebbins, G. L. *Variation and Evolution in Plants*. New York: Columbia University Press, 1950. An advanced discussion of the subject.

Swanson, C. P. *Cytology and Cytogenetics*. Englewood Cliffs, N. J.: Prentice-Hall, Inc., 1957. For the reader who wants further information on chromosome structure and behavior.

Wilson, E. B. *The Cell in Development and Heredity*, 3rd ed. New York: The Macmillan Company, 1924. A monumental synthesis of genetics, cytology, and development, written by the man to whom Morgan et al. dedicated their book.

GLOSSARY

Adaptation. Harmonious adjustment to environmental conditions. May refer to the manner by which adjustment is achieved; for instance, wings are an adaptation for flight—they adapt the organism for flight.

Allele. One or more alternative genes that are situated at the same locus in homologous chromosomes and are active in the same developmental process. A haploid organism has a single representative allele, a diploid has two, from the total number existing in the population as a whole.

Anaphase. Stage of cell division during which sister chromatids or homologous chromosomes separate and move polewards.

Antheridium. Male gamete-producing structure.

Bisexual. Bearing both kinds of gametes. Such organisms are thus all of a kind (monomorphic). Plants may be referred to as *monoecious* when stamens and ovules are borne in different flowers of the same plant.

Centromere. See *Kinetochore.*

Chiasma (plural, *chiasmata*). The point of attachment of homologous chromosomes after repulsion in meiotic prophase, caused by a change of chromatid-pairing partner.

Chromatid. One of the substituent strands of a chromosome; chromatids carry identical genetic material and are similar morphologically. At prophase, chromosomes normally have two functional chromatids.

Chromosome. Gene-bearing, thread-like structure in cell nucleus, composed of DNA and protein.

Clone. Population of genetically identical organisms.

Complementation. Cooperation by two genes or genomes resulting in development of a property that neither working alone can bring about.

Constitutive enzymes. Those whose presence is not affected by external conditions.

Controlling gene. A gene that controls the time and rate of action of structural genes.

Crossing-over. Physical exchange of chromatin between chromatids.

Cytokinesis. Division or cleavage of cytoplasmic portion of a cell, as distinct from nuclear division.

Dikaryon. Stable binucleate state of Basidiomycetes.

Dimorphism. Existence of two forms. In sexual dimorphism there is a male, sperm-producing form and a separate female, egg-producing form.

Dioecious. See *Unisexual.*

Diploid. Containing two full complements of homologous chromosomes.

Diplontic. Having a life cycle in which the products of meiosis behave directly as gametes.

Dominance. Prevalence of a gene or its associated character over its allele or associated character.

Epigenesis. Development in which differences are built on differences.

Epistasis. Dominance of one gene over another, nonallelic gene; opposite of *hypostasis.*

Eukaryota. The large group of animals and plants whose cells have typical chromosomes, nuclear membranes, and plastids.

Factor (genetic). Formerly, the hypothetical agent in cells responsible for development; now known to be DNA genes.

Filial. Pertaining to generations coming after a parental one; offspring.

Fitness. The measure of the effectiveness of reproduction—that is, contribution to ensuing generations.

Gametangium. Gamete-producing cell.

Gene. Discrete unit that directs development; purine and pyrimidine sequences within the DNA molecule that direct synthesis of specific RNA molecules and have effects both in and outside the nucleus.

Generation time. Average time between generations.

Genetic death. Death due to intrinsic failure in the genetic mechanism.

Genetic system. Complex of factors determining the balance between coherence and recombination of hereditary factors.

Genetics. Study of the nature and mechanism of inheritance.

Genome. The total chromosomal or genic makeup of an organism.

Genotype. Genetic makeup.

Haplo-diplontic. Having a life cycle in which both the products of meiosis and the zygote undergo mitotic growth before producing gametes and meiospores respectively.

Haplontic. Having a life cycle in which meiosis occurs in the zygote.

Haploid. Containing one full complement of chromosomes or genetic material.

Heterokaryon. Mycelium with nuclei of two or more genotypes inside it.

Heterozygous. Literally, forming different kinds of zygotes on self-fertilization; more generally, having unlike alleles.

Homokaryon. Mycelium with just one kind of nucleus in it.

Homologous. As applied genetically, having parallel though not necessarily identical action, controlling common physiological or developmental processes. Homologous chromosomes pair at meiosis.

Homologues. Chromosomes bearing similar gene sets that synapse during meiosis. Usually they are morphologically alike. In a diploid organism, one homologue is derived from each parent.

Homozygous. Literally, forming one kind of zygote on self-fertilization; more generally, having the genes of a gene pair (alleles) similar.

Hybrid. (noun) The progeny of a cross between two species, races, lines, or individuals of different genetic constitution; (adj.) heterozygous.

Hypostasis. Recessiveness of one gene to another, non-allelic gene.

Inducible enzymes. Those whose production can be evoked or suppressed by appropriate conditions.

Interphase. Stage of cell life during which metabolism and synthesis occur but no visible evidence of division exists.

Inversion. Alteration in sequence of genes in a chromosome.

Karyogamy. Fusion of nuclei.

Kinetochore (or *centromere*). Point of attachment of spindle fiber on chromosome.

Life cycle. Process of development involved in the perpetuation of an organismic population.

Linkage. Inheritance of characters in association with one another, explained by association of genes in a chromosome or DNA molecule; the opposite of segregation.

Locus. The site in chromosomes at which homologous genes occur.

Mating type. Breeding property of an organism, dependent on the allele carried, which determines mating ability.

Meiosis. Cell division in which chromosomes are reduced from the diploid to the haploid number and recombination usually occurs.

Meiospore. Haploid cell, resulting from meiosis, which undergoes mitotic divisions to produce a gamete-bearing multicellular structure (*gametophyte*).

Messenger RNA. Ribonucleic acid produced from DNA genes in the nucleus; it migrates to the cytoplasmic ribosomes and serves as template for protein synthesis there.

Metabolite. A product of metabolism.

Metaphase. Stage of cell division during which chromosomes are held in the equatorial plane.

Mitosis. Cell division producing daughter cells genetically similar to one another and to the parent cell.

Mitospore. Haploid or diploid cell, resulting from mitotic division, which undergoes mitotic growth to reproduce the kind of organism from which it arose.

Monoecious. See *Bisexual*.

Multiple alleles. Alleles that exist in a diversity of states rather than simply the classical dominant and recessive forms.

Mutation. Spontaneous, permanent, heritable change in organisms.

Oogonium. Female gamete-producing cell (*gametangium*).

Operator gene. One of the controlling genes that govern activity of structural genes beside them.

Ovulate. Bearing ovules; frequently refers to flowers that have only ovules, no stamens.

Phenotype. Post-developmental appearance or condition of an individual.

Plasmogamy. Fusion of cytoplasm of two cells.

Pleiotropic. Affecting development of more than one character simultaneously.

Polyploidy. Bearing of more than the normal chromosome number.

Position effect. Influence of gene position on gene function.

Prometaphase. Stage of cell division in which the spindle forms and the duplicated chromosomes move to the equatorial plane.

Propagule. Agent of dissemination; it may be unicellular or multicellular.

Prophase. First visible stage of cell division wherein duplicated chromosomes shorten and thicken, and nucleolus and nuclear membrane disappear.

Pseudoalleles. Genes that appear to reside at the same locus because they are closely linked.

Pure line. Stock of the same genetic constitution and homozygous for all gene pairs.

Recessiveness. Condition in which a gene is not expressed when in association with its dominant allele.

Recombination. Formation of new gene combinations.

Recombination within linkage groups. Segregation of genes (characters) that are usually linked. It is explained by crossing-over of chromosomal material.

Regulator gene. One of the controlling genes that act on the operator gene. They may be located anywhere in the genome.

Segregation. Separation of alleles or homologues at meiosis.

Selection (natural). Process whereby certain forms die off and are replaced by others.

Selective advantage. An advantage in the struggle for survival—that is, in natural selection.

Self-fertile. Having gametes and reproductive organs that permit fusion of gametes derived from the same parent organism.

Self-incompatibility. Failure of pollen to grow on the style of the parental plant.

Sex linkage. Inheritance of characters having no functional relevance to sex along with sex. It is explained by linkage of genes in the chromosome bearing sex-determining genes.

Sexual. Being capable of recombining genetic material.

Somatic. Referring to the body or vegetative cells—as opposed to the germ or generative cells, which give rise to gametes.

Staminate. Having stamens only in flowers.

Structural gene. Gene that serves ultimately as template for proteinaceous enzyme; has a cytoplasmic effect.

Synapsis. Side-by-side alignment of homologous chromosomes.

Syngamy. Fusion of gametes.

Telophase. Stage of cell division during which chromatids uncoil and return to invisibility; nucleolus and nuclear membrane are reconstituted.

Test cross. Cross of a hybrid to the homozygous recessive parent.

Transformation. Permanent change of genotype of a bacterium in the direction of another following its growth in a medium containing the latter's DNA.

Translocation. Exchange of chromatin between nonhomologous chromosomes.

Unisexual. Bearing only one kind of gamete. Such organisms are thus dimorphic (male and female). In the case of plants, they are frequently referred to as dioecious; staminate flowers are borne on one plant and ovulate flowers on another.

INDEX